Keeping Domestic Geese

Barbara Soanes

BLANDFORD

Blandford
An imprint of Cassell,
Villiers House, 41–47 Strand, London WC2N 5JE

This edition first published in the U.K. 1992

Previously published in the U.K. 1980

Distributed in Australia by
Capricorn Link (Australia) Pty Ltd.
P.O. Box 665, Lane Cove, NSW 2066

British Library Cataloguing in Publication Data
Soanes, Barbara
    Keeping domestic geese. 2nd. ed.
    1. Livestock : Geese. Cars & management
    I. Title
    636.598

ISBN 0–7137–2265–7

Printed and bound in Great Britain by
Biddles Ltd, Guildford and King's Lynn

Contents

[5]

Preface

Geese are the easiest domestic creatures of all to keep, but for many years there had been no readily available up-to-date book on the subject to help those many people who would very much like to keep them, if only they knew how. That was my main reason for writing the book, first time around, in 1980. At the time, I expressed the hope that the book would answer many questions often asked about geese, and enable everyone to get as much pleasure from keeping them as I have done.

Since its first publication, I have been surprised and delighted by the enquiries and letters that my publisher and I have received – from all over the world – in response to the book. In order to satisfy the many requests *and* to introduce the delights and rewards of keeping geese to a new audience, this new edition has been produced.

BS 1990

Acknowledgements

I am very grateful to the many people who contributed either photographs or information for this book. In particular I would like to thank the following: Mr Christopher Marler, President of the British Waterfowl Association; the British Waterfowl Association, Market Place, Haltwhistle, Northumberland; M. Alex Wiltzer, President of the French Société d'Aviculture; W. Jarominski, Poland; S. Pimenov, the Russian All Union Scientific Technological Institute of Poultry Breeding; Mr Prosser, veterinary surgeon and avian specialist; Herr Willi Kumler, Germany; Domnul Georgi Stanescu, Romania; The Ottawa Department of Agriculture, Canada; Mr Vernon Jackson; Mr John Hall; Mrs Anne Starey; Mrs Freda Stilwell; Mr and Mrs G. Allen; Mr Collinson; Mr and Mrs Whittick; Mr Peter Hayford; and last but by no means least my especial thanks to my husband and son, who have helped me so much with every aspect of my consuming interest in goose-keeping.

Goose Topography

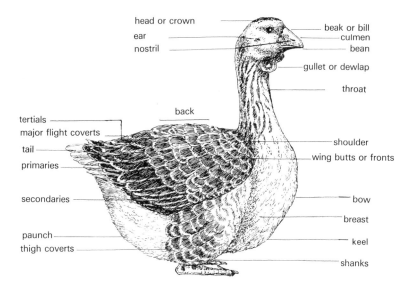

head or crown — beak or bill
ear — culmen
nostril — bean
gullet or dewlap
throat
back
tertials
major flight coverts
tail — shoulder
primaries — wing butts or fronts
secondaries — bow
breast
paunch — keel
thigh coverts — shanks

[1]
History and Connections with Man

Early man, around the period of the last ice age (20,000–10,000 B.C.) must have seen many flocks of geese, forced southwards by the spreading ice. He was doubtless interested in the feeding flocks as the possible source of his next meal, but his weapons were inadequate to kill such wary creatures, with their ever vigilant sentinels posted around the flock. There are no known cave paintings or carvings of geese from this earliest period. There is little doubt that the real connection between man and goose began as man himself changed from being a hunter, perpetually roaming in pursuit of herds of deer and buffalo, to a more settled pastoral and agricultural way of life. This took place around the period 8000 B.C., as the ice sheets were retreating again.

By this date, in Iraq, Syria and Israel, man began to cultivate the first grain crops, and for the first time he had enough food for himself and perhaps to fatten his geese and animals as well. The stubble left after harvesting attracted the regular migrations of Greylag and other breeds, who fed off the grain which had escaped the harvesters. This brought geese and farmers together for the first time, and it happened annually.

The first domesticated geese might well have been casualties. Such accidents are fairly common, especially as wild geese fly up to 5,500 miles in one migration, and landing safely to rest and feed when in large numbers can be hazardous. Alternatively, the reason may have been the increasing prowess with the stone and sling amongst the peoples of the Fertile Crescent. Such a method would stun but not necessarily kill; and such captured birds, and any subsequent goslings, would have been pinioned or had their flight feathers cut off to make escape impossible.

The first drawings and carvings appear in the Middle East. Geese are painted and carved on the walls of Egyptian tombs as semi-deities. The earliest of these bas-relief carvings is dated 4500 B.C. These carved geese were obviously of two distinct species: the Egyptian goose and a type of Greylag or Lesser White-fronted goose such as can be found in Europe today.

The first positive evidence of man's control and domestication of geese is to be found in Mesopotamia (present-day Iraq), where the Greylag and Lesser White-fronted geese still migrate for the winter. On a limestone plaque from Ur, dating from 2400 B.C., the peasants are shown leading or driving their animals as offerings to give to the King, Mesanipadda. Cattle, sheep, donkeys, horses and geese are clearly carved, accompanied by dogs.

By 1600 B.C. in Egypt, a live Greylag goose was considered to be a fit present for Queen Hatshepsut, in company with a live pelican. A bas-relief carving depicts the presenter wisely holding the beaks to avoid pecking!

In Europe, the continued retreat of the ice sheets from 8000 B.C. onwards encouraged the spread of settled farming, with the cultivation of cereal crops becoming well established under the increasingly warmer climatic conditions. The summer breeding grounds of the six largest breeds of the Anserinae family (Greylag, Bean, Pink-footed, Snow, Lesser White-fronted and White-fronted) gradually shifted northwards following the retreating ice. Today these breeding grounds are on the most northerly quiet land areas of Europe and Russia. They extend from Greenland, Iceland and Norway, through Finland fringing the White Sea, to Novaya Zemlya and Siberia.

The Greylag, considered to be at least the chief ancestor of most of the world's domesticated breeds of geese, has always been the most common goose, and has always had more extensive breeding grounds than the other breeds. By 1000 B.C. Greylag bred all over southern, central and northern Europe and Asia, before man came in sufficient numbers continually to disturb and disrupt their breeding areas.

All geese are at their most vulnerable in the breeding season, when they have young to guard. Just when these young become more able to fend for themselves the adults lose their ability to fly, with the moulting of their flight feathers. This vulnerability is emphasized in that in Iceland, in 500 B.C., the inhabitants built stone-walled horse-shoe shaped enclosures on the remote plateau of Hofsjokull, into which they learnt to drive the flightless, helpless flocks of geese every year. Some were slaughtered, and some undoubtedly kept as domestic flocks. These enclosures are still there, and the plateau is still one of the main breeding grounds for Pink-footed geese today.

As the climatic belts shifted northwards large numbers of Greylag moved their principal winter pasturage northwards from Mesopotamia into Greece, Turkey and Italy. By 600 B.C. in Greece, Aesop wrote of domestic geese as commonplace. The birds were widely kept and in large flocks. Aristotle wrote of the general interest in poultry-keeping in Greece in 400 B.C., and tells us that the Greeks had been much interested in artificial incubation which they had learnt of in Egypt, and where it had been practised for many years. In both China and Egypt artificial incubation was already on a commercial scale.

By 388 B.C., the famous Roman geese had saved their city from attack. Geese in Italy were kept by that date in such large domesticated flocks that they were an ordinary dish for a nobleman's table. These large flocks were plucked, live, twice a year for down to stuff cushions and bedding. Goose quills from the flight feathers were used as pens as early as 500 B.C. in Italy. Goose fat was used as an ointment or a salve against chest ailments.

Caesar reported that on his visit to England in 55 B.C. the primitive British had large flocks of geese, which appeared to be held sacred and were never eaten. By 9 B.C. when Drusus, acting for Emperor Augustus, attempted to subdue all the tribes north of Italy up to the River Elbe in Germany, northern Europeans had numerous flocks of grey and white geese. Like the Romans, they had bred pure white geese from the 'sports' amongst the Greylag. By A.D. 30 Pliny reported that the best of the German-reared flocks, obviously famous by then, were imported from there to

Rome to add new size and vigour to existing flocks. These birds were pure white and plainly considered very fine, and they were herded all the way across the Alps to Rome, with their feet dipped in tar for protection.

Claudius, in A.D. 43, wrote of fine extra large grey flocks of domesticated geese in France. This is possibly the first mention of what are now known as Toulouse, Landes and Alsace grey geese. It would seem that the white flocks seen by Caesar and Claudius in Germany, which were good enough to be imported into Italy, must have been Germany's foundation stock of Embdens.

Even today the Greylag frequently produces white offspring 'sports', and it is not hard to envisage the earliest goose-raisers following a deliberate policy of retaining only the white birds for their flocks. It is also a well documented fact that the live plucking of grey geese leads to an ever increasing proportion of white feathers in the re-growth. This discovery must have pleased the Romans, who admired white geese.

It is interesting to note that in those areas where today the Greylags choose a winter habitat (sometimes with a few members of another breed) we humans have also chosen to keep large numbers of domestic geese. For example, Poland, with its regular visiting migrations of geese, has a numerous domestic goose population, kept for the European demand for table geese. In 1977 their flocks totalled over 10 million geese.

Other European areas of importance for breeding domestic geese, as well as being wintering grounds for wild geese, are Bulgaria, Moravia and Romania. In Romania (2 million geese) these flocks are kept mainly on lands bordering the River Danube. Hungary (1 million), Czechoslovakia (250,000), Yugoslavia (2 million) and much of the Ukraine also have large domestic flocks; both state owned and privately owned. In France (3 million) the southern *départements* of Gironde, Haute Gironde, Gers and the Landes have the largest numbers of geese, and this has been so since Roman times. The white goose of Poitou and the grey Landes, Alsace and Toulouse are the most popular breeds.

Northern Germany (1 million), Denmark (250,000) and Holland (120,000) have large commercial flocks, and many smaller

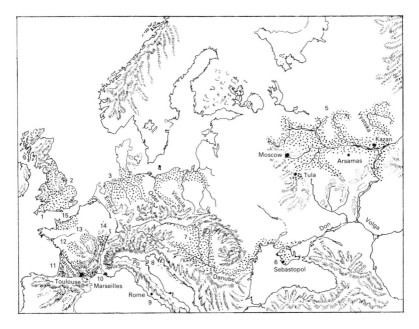

Areas of origin for domestic goose breeds in Europe and the USSR. 1. West of England. 2. Whites, Saddlebacks. 3. Embden. 4. Pomeranian. 5. Tula, Kholmogorsk, Arsamas. 6. Sebastopol. 7. Danubian. 8. Padovan. 9. Roman. 10. Toulouse. 11. Landes. 12. Poitou. 13. Bourbonnais. 14. Alsace. 15. Normandy.

ones owned by smallholder and farmer. Israel is also of rising importance as a producer of geese; flocks have been established there for some years now, and are prospering well. Goose production in the USA is now nearly 500,000 birds a year, with the central states, stretching latitudinally from California in the west to Pennsylvania in the east, having the largest proportion of the total goose population.

In the British Isles, all of the rural areas, with their usually abundant grass and water, are particularly suited to geese. The MAFF figures for England in 1977 were 113,582 geese, on holdings of usually 2 acres or more; in other words from Registered Agricultural Holdings. Nevertheless, there are unregistered holdings of 3–5 acres for which there are no figures, as well as those of 1 acre of less. So there is undoubtedly a 'hidden' goose population which may possibly be up to half as many geese again as the official figures show.

A second interesting fact is that, according to the 1977 Agricultural returns, the MAFF Eastern Region (Norfolk, Suffolk, Hertfordshire, Essex, Cambridgeshire, Bedfordshire and Greater London) had the largest number of geese, with 26,218. Thus once again man has chosen to rear domestic geese in an area regularly chosen by wild migrating and breeding geese for many thousands of years. This Eastern Region is a very long established area for the rearing of both geese and turkeys. It is mentioned as such in various writings since the Middle Ages. Certainly by 1820 it was recorded that geese and turkeys from this area were herded down south to London, a distance of 80 miles or more, with their feet dipped in tar just as was done by the Romans in 9 B.C.

A hundred years later, such flocks of East Anglian geese, numbering 8000 and more, are recorded, and some of the elderly people living in Essex can remember these huge flocks passing through with dogs and drovers, bound for London's Smithfield Market.

The south-west of England (Cornwall, Devon, Somerset, Dorset, Wiltshire, Avon, Gloucestershire) has the next largest population of geese, with 16,911. Wales has 16,221, and the other regions have about 10,000 each. The largest sized flocks are found in East Anglia, and contain up to 1000 birds, but there are many flocks with 100 or so breeding birds in England as a whole.

The first geese to be kept domestically in the USA were English Greys, Whites and Saddlebacks taken over by those practical emigrants, the Pilgrim Fathers (1620), from Britain. These birds would have been from the same west-country stock from which the auto-sexing West of England geese developed. ('Auto-sexing', or 'sex-linked', means that the sex of the bird can be determined visually without resort to internal examination.) The Fathers' ship *Mayflower* has listed on bills of lading these geese, which became the foundation stock from which New England flocks derived, until the importation 200 years later of 'new, larger' Embdens and Toulouse from Europe.

[14]

In Asia and Eastern Europe there are also very many geese kept domestically, ranging from surprisingly arid areas, such as Khirgizia, to southern humid China. In the latter country they are kept extensively, under governmental encouragement, as part of a general striving to farm in a 'total' unspecialized way, so that each village commune has a flock.

In Russia, goose-rearing has always been a traditional branch of agriculture. Pre-revolutionary Russia led the world in the numbers of breeders and in the production of table-birds. In 1960–61, 2.3 million fully-grown geese were being kept in the public sector, and although numbers fell sharply in 1968 the introduction of factory methods of keeping geese has halted the decline. In 1978 the numbers had risen back up to 752,000. Not accounted in these figures are the numbers of geese on private holdings attached to collective farms, which are estimated to be considerable. The most popular pure breed is the large Kholmo-gorsk, which is frequently crossed with the Tula for table-bird production. The Christmas goose (Rozhdestvenskii) is still tradi-tional in the Central provinces and Volga-Vyatskii region but not elsewhere.

The varieties of domestic geese in Eastern Europe and Russia have derived from the Eastern Greylag (*Anser anser rubrirostris*) which has a pink beak as distinct from the orange beak (or bill) of the western Greylag's descendants. These basically eastern genes show not only in the Kholmogorsk, Tula and Arsamas of Russia, but also in the Pomeranian and frequently the Sebastopol, the Brecon and the American Buff, although western breed re-quirements do not approve of pink beaks in two of these breeds.

The fact is that the modern domestic breeds of geese have un-doubtedly evolved from many and various cross-breedings between the six largest wild-goose breeds (not solely the two varieties of Greylag) in the past as well as being influenced by man's own interventions.

[2]
How to Start

Before buying, first assess the facilities you possess for your geese. How much land is available? Take into account that they may need to be housed, and that the housing is best situated within the same area. Is there already a constant supply of running water, however small, or a pond? If there is, you will be freed from considerable daily effort, and could therefore keep more in number. Is the grazing good, with few weeds? Some breeds are very poor at foraging and will consistently reject all weeds to eat, while others will relish a few. Finally, consider your neighbours. Some breeds, although suitable for a small garden, are very inclined to be noisy all day, whereas others are nearly silent.

Secondly, you must decide whether you wish to keep geese to sell their offspring as future breeding stock or whether you have enough land to consider launching your enterprise into the table-bird meat market. As a guide, 1 acre (see Appendix I for metric equivalents) will support 20 light to medium breed adults and 10–15 heavy breeds, but only under the best possible grazing and watering conditions. This makes no allowance for the provision of grassland on which to rear any goslings.

If you are interested in the table-bird market, ask locally whether there is or has been an interest in a large or a small Christmas goose, and, just in case you later decide that you do not wish to kill and prepare your table-birds yourselves, enquire from your local butchers whether they would be interested in buying from you and what current range of price could you expect to get per pound based on the previous year's prices.

Of course, if you can and will kill and sell oven-ready geese yourselves, either for Michaelmas or Christmas, the 'middle man' is removed from the operation. This will bring you greater profits, but you will need to advertise your business as widely as possible and well in advance.

It may be that all the land available to be set aside for your geese is little more than a medium to large garden. This can still offer you several possibilities. You may keep your geese as grass cutters and family friends: either eat the eggs yourselves, feed the eggs to the dogs or other livestock or sell them in the local market. Alternatively, let the mother goose hatch them if she will; the goslings at a day old or thereabouts will always find a ready sale.

For such medium-sized gardens or areas, a pair or trio of parent birds will be enough to start with. From a pair of geese, the off-spring will not be numerous enough to put you in the table-bird business on any footing other than supplying yourselves, neighbours and friends with oven-ready dinners, but even so will provide an income and cheap, delicious meat.

The other alternative to meat-producing is to rear breeding stock for sale. Provided that you have chosen your pure-bred parent birds wisely from reputable sources, and provided that the birds comfortably meet the pure breed requirements, there will be a steady yearly demand for your young stock at considerably higher prices than cross-breeds will fetch.

On a garden or large lawn, it is even wiser to limit the number of breeds to just one, as penning to keep several breeds separate in the mating season is very difficult to do. Even if this is achieved, the active fliers will defy your efforts to contain them, and the purity of the resultant goslings will be in doubt.

Cross-breeds offer rather fewer challenges to the breeder than pure breeds, for they come in such varied colours, shapes and sizes that judging them on any basis is often an arbitrary business. Nevertheless, cross-bred goslings hatch rather more easily, and are often more vigorous when very young.

Bearing in mind the above factors, turn next to the section on breeds, and observing the information as well as the photographs

[17]

you will be able to make your selection, best suited to your individual requirements. Contact one or two reputable breeders telling them exactly what you require, and enquiring the price. If at all possible, try to arrange to see the parent stock, or at least photographs of them. Pure-bred stock, if it is good, is expensive to buy and may have to come from a considerable distance. You will not want the disappointment of inferior stock having to be expensively railed back again!

You may have the choice of buying eggs, or day-old goslings, or birds at any age to adulthood. Adults would have already had at least a year's breeding and probably will be 'fixed' in a pair, trio or set.

If you hope to buy pure breeds, note that the better breeders very rarely sell eggs or day-olds or even birds younger than 12 weeks, because as breeders they want to retain, for the upkeep of the high standards of their own flock, the very best birds of each season. All too often it is almost impossible to tell how good every gosling will be until that age. Moreover, most breeders, whose reputations must be upheld, would also not sell the weaklings of every hatch, but would prefer to kill off such specimens for the freezer. The later selling age does prevent customers being dissatisfied.

Nevertheless, it may pay you to ask, as the initial outlay on young goslings is obviously much less. Just bear in mind that by so buying you are taking a gamble on quality and must accept what develops. If you buy from the local market in this way, you will be best advised to buy from elsewhere after you have sexed the young ones, unless the seller is sure that the gander is unrelated to the females. This hurdle can be avoided by buying from the better breeders, who always endeavour to sell unrelated pairs or trios.

It is probably wiser to save your money and buy birds of 4 months and older. From this age upwards, most breeders can assure you that you are being supplied with the right sex and with unrelated ganders, and you will be saved the troubles of rearing, brooding and seeing that the goslings do not die in adverse weather for your first season, thus saving money in the end.

Many people are actually offered eggs free to put under broody hens, and the hen often hatches off fine goslings. Such eggs, however, are not usually from pure stock, and the eventual shape, size or beauty of such goslings when they attain adulthood is not usually very remarkable.

If you still desire table-bird production, for which the hardier cross-bred goslings are so suitable, I would advise buying pure-bred parents—one of each breed. The most common cross is the Embden × Toulouse. If your plot of land is large, an active Embden gander put with Toulouse females will give you more goslings than the other way around. This is because Embden ganders are very vigorous, and Toulouse females lay more eggs than their Embden counterparts.

Bearing in mind, however, that their more numerous offspring will have to be allowed plenty of grass for rearing them until the fattening period, in gardens up to a quarter of an acre, I would not recommend this arrangement, but rather putting a Toulouse gander with an Embden goose. In this combination, the gander will admittedly not have so many eggs to fertilize, but he will be more friendly and far quieter than an Embden. It will also keep the goslings to the right number for your available grazing.

It is not wise to buy cross-bred geese from the outset because although first-time crossed birds are usually of a thoroughly satis-factory size, sometimes larger than their pure parents, subsequent breeding between crossed birds produces a continuous deteriora-tion in the size of each succeeding generation, until they are almost back to Greylag weight (9 lb). It is best to keep the pure-bred parents and always use their cross-bred offspring for the table-bird production, thus ensuring that each year's goslings are of a good size.

Note that all young breeders do not reach their full lay in their first year, and fewer goslings may be hatched then than in any following year, even though those that do may be splendid birds. This is the reason that buying older geese is often the quickest way of actually getting started. Indeed, an older gander with young female geese frequently produces the best results for the first year because he is experienced at mating.

Moreover, the results of experiments with individual pen matings at the Experimental Goose Station in Quebec province, Canada, and also at the Ohio Experimental Station, USA, show very positively that geese lay more and larger eggs in their second, third and subsequent years than when yearlings. Even more important is the fact that these eggs hatch better. These Stations quote a 10 per cent increase in goslings hatched between first and second year geese, and a 60 per cent increase in egg production in the second year. Buying an older goose may be a very good investment indeed. The sad thing is that the gander may have to be replaced after 9 or 10 years by a younger one, as his fertility does gradually decline after that. The females go on laying until they are 100 years old, if they live that long (and some do), although the number of eggs drops to about 8 a season, instead of 30–40 in most breeds and strains at their prime.

[3]
Selection and Control of Breeding Stock

Choosing the adult breeding stock is one of the most important steps in goose-keeping. It is helpful to take your books on geese with you for reference. The photographs in the books usually show the better specimens and these can be used as a guide to quality. The breed requirements are very important. If requirements for say Brecon Buffs are that the head, neck, wings and back should all be in shades of fawny-buff, then any white patches on these parts constitute a fault, and such birds should be avoided. So read well before you set out, and in general look for fit, typical specimens, with correctly coloured feathering, beaks, legs and eyes.

The eyes should show an alertness, as should the general bearing of the bird, indicating vigour and vitality. The tails should be carried quite well up, and the wings should be neatly folded across the back. As far as temperament goes, except during the spring mating season when ganders can rightly be expected to be fierce to strangers, do not begin by buying a gander that attacks its present owner. Such a purchase would be an unnecessary mistake and would put off the whole family; most ganders are very amiable and affectionate to their owners. They may hiss, but on its own this is purely a warning to humans not to hurt them or their mates.

There is no harm whatever in picking out a large individual as long as he looks fit, if size is what you and the breed requirements demand. Indeed, for Exhibition or top quality Toulouse, Embdens, Africans and American Buffs, size is important and at

Flock of Embdens (Mrs A. A. Starey). This attractive outdoor scene typifies the rewards to be gained from domestic goose-keeping.

least one of the pair ought to be as large a bird as you can select, provided that it does not show any serious faults or deformities. If slim and elegant feathers are required, buy with this in mind.

When amalgamating geese into a group, you are bound to hear much about 'in-breeding'. Most of the best flocks are or have been in-bred at some point. This means that there has been a deliberate policy of 'breeding back' son to mother, daughter to father. It is a recognized fact that this is the way to ensure that certain characteristics, such as size, remain constant or 'fixed' in the flock.

Such flocks are called 'closed' flocks, because outside strains which may bring with them different hereditary genes are excluded. This is undoubtedly the way in which colour and size have been altered from that of the original wild goose. So in many ways this method is desirable; only if you appear to have in your closed flock a bird, or birds, who have some bad faults which you see recurring should you reconsider your breeding arrangements. Brother and sister matings, however, are considerably less successful than father, daughter, mother, son, with any inherent faults being brought forward quite frequently, and so it is best to start off with unrelated geese, as it widens the gene-pool for the future.

As you look to make your selection, try to determine whether they appear to be on good grazing. If they are, and they are small birds, they are probably a small strain. If they have been on poor food, it may be that they or their goslings could achieve a greater size under better conditions. Remember that only the larger breeds tend to go on growing for as many as 3 years, slowly and generally thickening up, but medium and small breeds will hardly blossom at all after a year old.

If you are going to breed table-birds, the inclusion of a white or even a buff bird (preferably a gander) amongst your greys will help to ensure a higher proportion of white or nearly white off-spring. This, in turn, makes a nicer-looking pink-fleshed bird when plucked. (It makes no improvement to the taste, incidentally. Indeed, for home consumption the darker-feathered birds give darker but tastier meat. The buying public in general, however, likes a pink, polyfilm-wrapped look.)

If you are not buying a well-established looking adult 'set' of geese, it is advisable to purchase and put together your adults from different sources, as soon as you can in the autumn. Never leave it until the spring, because adult ganders vary enormously in their willingness to accept strange females as mates, and some-times reject one completely. Such marital disagreements must be solved well in advance of the next spring mating season, or else there will be few fertile eggs and a disappointed owner.

It is usually advised that with the light breeds, such as Romans, Sebastopols and Brown and White Chinas, four or five geese may be successfully put with one gander. With the medium breeds such as Pilgrim, Brecon Buffs, Pomeranians, and such crossings as Embden × Toulouse, one gander to three or four geese is successful. With the heavier breeds such as Toulouse, Embdens, Africans and American Buffs, one gander to two or three geese can be advised; but even here it must be said that Embden ganders, although very large, are frequently very active sexually, and when young may well run with three females.

On the other hand, Toulouse are often increasingly faithful to just one goose out of a pair of female geese, and pair matings are often the happiest solution. If there are two females with him, one becomes progressively ignored and sad, and the owner obtains no fertile eggs from her.

The problem may occur when one goose from a set dies, and the owner wishes to introduce another strange female. Such a newcomer can have a very bad time from the attacks of the older established females, and the gander may well refuse to mate with her. The solution to this, if it occurs, is to take the gander away from all the females, and put the females in a smallish makeshift pen. Give limited room so that fighting is difficult, and leave them in this until any animosity dies down. This will happen quite soon after the gander is taken out of sight, and, if possible, hearing. At the end of 3 or 4 days, try putting them back together; if this is not successful, give the arrangement another few days.

Once you have a settled pair, trio or set, it is prudent to leave them in a pen (large) on their own for their first season, especially if you are breeding geese for sale as large Exhibition birds for stock, and have arranged each pairing carefully so as to breed particular points and qualities into the goslings. If this is not your special purpose, and a general mixing of several pairs of geese does no damage to your aims, then 2 or 3 months may suffice for each set to cement its relationships before meeting the others. The better cemented these relationships are, the fewer fights between ganders (which cause a lowering in fertility) will happen in the spring. Many ganders are intelligent and calm enough to keep out of disputes, and apart from the odd gander who is an awkward customer different sets of geese will run happily together after the spring is over. If sleeping in the open, they will settle down in their own special places, quite amicably, at night.

For those intending to achieve better results from their stock, however, I would still advise trying to give each set their own quarters, even if not a separate pen. It is not as difficult as it sounds; but it does necessitate giving a name to at least the gander in each set, for then, after 2 or 3 days of uncertainty, they learn to come when you call, to lead or drive them to their correct night-time quarters.

A long bamboo rod, such as those sold by gardening shops for runner-bean growing, will help point and train the sets in their own directions. They quickly learn, after the first night's panic, to go to their own house, and seem very happy to have family privacy, especially in the spring when the geese are laying. Given such arrangements, the female or females normally choose to make their nests in their own homes, thus giving the owner some idea of whose eggs, and therefore whose goslings, are whose. Of course, however, it does happen that ganders mate with females out of their own sets during the day, and so you still cannot be quite positive about the parentage of the goslings. The best method therefore appears to be separate houses and separate grassy pens. For example, where I once had a large area ($1\frac{1}{4}$ acres) where five pairs of Toulouse ran together, wire netting fences have been constructed to divide the whole into nine pens, each with access to the stream, and every pair now grazes separately. Four pens are unused, so that the birds can be 'rotated' when a paddock becomes exhausted.

This obviously cannot be done with large numbers of geese, however, without considerable effort in fencing and organization. Once they have all stopped mating, they can then be run together, if required, until the new season approaches, by opening up the interconnecting gates.

This is a kind of 'trap-nesting' method. Trap-nesting is where each goose is confined to her own trap-doored cage until the owner notes the number or identity of the layer, as well as marking the eggs, before releasing her. This provides information such as which are the most prolific layers, whose strain has the least mortality at hatching, as well as other breeding factors, and is practised with success in Canada and the USA by some goose-breeders.

This is obviously a very scientific method of attaining the best results from a commercial point of view; it does, however, have its problems. Geese are by no means obliging about the time of day for laying eggs, and very few will voluntarily enter the traps.

Mr Schiltz of Bancroft, USA, is probably the leader in this field and has achieved increases in flock fertility, egg production and hatchability of around 36 per cent on average since he began in 1957. He works at present with over 1000 breeders, with a computer for selection purposes.

It is plain that for such methods to work really well a large flock, certainly of 100 or more, is necessary. The separate pens and housing method and trap-nesting are the only exact ways of eliminating from a flock those birds which give unsatisfactory results of one kind or another.

If records are kept of eggs laid, with identification marks put on the eggs as they are collected from each house or pen, it is an easy matter to see how many eggs each goose is laying. Even when these eggs go into the smallest of incubators (50 hen egg size) each batch of eggs from each set can be kept apart from the others by simple barriers of ½-inch gauge wire netting, which do not interfere with the working of the machine or the circulation of the warm air. These barriers, bent to shape round the different batches, will keep apart the newly-hatched goslings, giving you a chance to mark the goslings before letting them go into the brooder all together. Each batch will grow up with a permanent record of from which parents they came, even showing variations in vigour at hatch as well as other factors.

Both trap-nesting and the separation of pairs or trios, then, are for those looking for points of excellence. There is no need at all to encumber yourself with either method if you are prepared to accept what comes, under more free circumstances. You will still get decent birds: one or two good ones, some average and some poor from every hatch. As always, it just depends on how interested each goose-owner is. After all, many people welcome a non-standard size for the table-bird trade, as they often have orders for both large and small birds for Christmas, and like to be able to oblige on both counts.

[4]
Shelter, Housing, Penning and Water

Geese much prefer sleeping in the open. In the wild state, when the weather becomes too hot or too cold, geese begin their customary migrations to a more equable climate. Domestication means that they now have to cope with extreme temperatures unsuited to them, as well as no longer being able to fly away from predators lurking in the night.

If you are certain that no stray dogs, foxes, mink or other predators are in your locality, then you can provide very simple shelters just to give them a windbreak. Straw bales, erected in a line at right angles to the prevailing winds, or in an open-sided box shape, perhaps with weighted corrugated iron over the roof space, provide a cheap, quick shelter. Such a shelter will also be suitable to serve up the food in when it is snowing, and if very low temperatures ($-7°C$ [20°F] or less) occur, will prevent their feet, and in the case of Africans and Chinas their knobs (the fleshy protuberances at the top of the upper bill) from being frost-damaged. Double lengths of 1-inch gauge wire netting made into an open-sided box shape, with the gap between the netting filled with straw, reeds or bracken well pushed down to make compact, draught-proof walls is a very cheap alternative. It may need replacement stuffing every year or so.

Less sightly, but often obtainable from skips or rubbish dumps for nothing, are old wooden doors. These can be used equally well as walls or roofing and are often very solidly made. The sectional nature of a door-constructed house is often useful if the goose field has no natural shade from trees, bushes or hedges in summer;

Flock of Romans (G. Allen). Note the fine, smooth feathering of these birds, with their plump faces and quite short beaks.

the sides may be partly removed to give a good through draught, while the roof remains as a sunshade. In temperatures of 21 °C (70 °F) geese suffer very badly unless some shade is available. Indeed, they can cope with intense cold far better than with heat. Canvas awnings or brushwood can be fixed so that all-day shade is available, but if weather conditions are not too hot and arid the planting of trees improves the over-all appearance of the goose area, and also encourages any grass that does grow underneath the trees to stay green and fresh longer. Fruit trees are very good for many purposes: they are not too dense to discourage the grass, yet provide good shade after a couple of years from planting, as well as fruit.

Open-fronted buildings, such as tractor sheds, are suitable for shelters, as are old stables or outbuildings of any kind. Even a large dog kennel, with entrance modifications, will cope well with a pair of geese. Ideally, goose houses do not need to be more than 4 feet high, and require just enough turning space per bird to keep them and their house from becoming too dirty every night. An area of 8 ft × 6 ft would comfortably house 4–6 geese, according to size.

If you are not converting a building or old henhouse for use but are constructing your own model, before you start sawing cast an eye over your blueprint to see how easy mucking out will be. Do not have too low a ceiling to be able to straighten your back when cleaning out. It is best to keep the width from front to back to under 5 ft, or to the reach of a pitchfork.

HOUSING

Most goose-rearers, however, are not fortunate enough to live in an area totally free of predators, and so must protect their geese more extensively, especially from foxes.

Foxes will visit poultry yards and geese regularly at night, so care must always be taken. Dusk and dawn are when geese are most at risk, so do not leave them out too late. Early summer is a particularly dangerous time because the senior dog-foxes, having growing families to feed, are tempted to attack where they might otherwise be chary. Do not be tempted to place your faith in a very large, fierce gander; he will defend his geese as well as he can, but is very unlikely to be the victor. This will leave you with desolate, terrified females and no fertile eggs for that spring, as well as being a sad loss to yourselves. If you see that you start off with safe housing, your worries are over. In fact it is only in the matter of safe housing that any effort is needed in the business of keeping adult geese.

It is well to note that even 7-ft-high chain-link fencing has not always deterred a hungry fox, as well as the fact that it is prohibitively expensive over a large area. Only in conjunction with further barbed or electric wire fencing, leaning outwards above the chain-link, does this provide a foolproof compound against foxes (but even so not against mink and rats at hatching time). Therefore start with fox-, mink- and rat-proof housing, and then throughout the year, especially when the mother geese may start to nest in the corner of their houses, you can shut them in at night knowing that your geese, eggs and goslings will be safe until you let them out in the morning.

When constructing the roof of the goose-house, give it a slight angle so that rain runs off easily. Timber and galvanized iron are very suitable materials. If the corrugated is full of holes, pieces of sticky waterproof webbing, such as Sylglass, are useful when pressed down well on the upper surfaces, and a coat of black bitumastic underneath stops constant dripping. If the roof is made of wood, black bitumastic roofing felt protects it for many years. Black plastic is efficient even if it does not look very elegant. Tuck it over the leading edges well, in case of high winds.

Put a floor in every house: paving slabs, concrete, or chalk wetted and rammed down hard are the best of all; but, failing these, fix a $\frac{1}{2}$-inch to 1-inch netting floor to the bottom of the superstructure if resting on or near the ground, so that nothing harmful can tunnel up underneath. Check all door and window fittings; fill gaps in the woodwork with cement, battens, crumpled wire netting or wire wool. Nail flat galvanized tin to worm-eaten areas especially at or near ground level. Put wire netting over the windows, especially if they are not more than 2 feet from the ground, and see that no convenient branch, or other aid to easy access through the windows, is possible.

Alternatively, raise the whole structure at least 6 inches off the ground on bricks and give it a solid wooden floor, not slats, and then you will not need netting. The ramp, which is then necessary, will not cause any problems for the geese. Raising your housing has two advantages: you can see at a glance if anything has been trying to gnaw an entry, and you can lay down rat poison under the buildings and out of reach of the geese, to keep the ever-present rodent population down. Mink and rats are admittedly normally only a menace to young babies and goose eggs, but their enthusiasm for goslings (or ducklings) in particular leads them to great efforts to gain entry. The invasion by rats or mink of the sitting goose's home has an unsettling effect on her. In defence of her eggs, she and the gander often accidentally step on and break more, and you can hardly expect the mother to feel she can concentrate fully on hatching under those circumstances.

The siting of the houses should be on fairly well-drained land, and I prefer to have the housing quite near the house, rather than far away. It is less distance to go to put them in at night, and if you are allowing your geese to sit it is easier to keep an eye on things if you are close at hand. I always keep two houses and two penning areas nearest of all to the house, for the arrival of the goslings in the spring. These areas and houses are not used for the adult geese from January until about August, so that the goslings are under my very closest scrutiny for accidents, such as getting stuck in water bowls, or attacks from rooks, crows, buzzards and magpies.

As for bedding inside the houses, the babies up to about 8 weeks old are best on wood chips, which are exceptionally absorbent and easy to clean off the flooring. From that age onwards, straw is the best material, although care must be taken that there is no greyish mould inside the bale, as this can affect the respiratory systems in young birds. Otherwise, it makes a warm, cheap bedding, and finishes up on the garden as mulch or manure. For the sake of health and flooring, try not to let the bedding get too wet and filthy. If you have the right amount of space for the birds in each house, you will only need to spread a fresh, shallow layer of straw on top of the old every 2 days or so in winter, and in summer, with longer daylight hours, far less often.

Bracken, a traditional bedding material in hilly parts of Britain, is fine, but it must be completely dried. Hay can be used, but it is always more expensive than straw and does not absorb the droppings as well.

In the winter months, provided that the floors can take the weight, it does no harm to keep adding fresh straw until the bedding is a foot or so deep. In extra cold, snowy weather, a thick layer helps warm up their feet quickly when they go to bed.

PENNING

If you wish to restrict the birds to a specific place for grazing, 2-inch gauge wire netting, 3 feet high, is very satisfactory, using tanalized fence posts of 2–3-inch diameter. Tanalizing helps keep the posts in good condition for years. For very small goslings, or growers put next to a pen of adults, 1-inch gauge is best, as they can get their heads or beaks painfully pecked by the adults if they can get their heads through.

When buying very active breeds which you intend to separate into sets, see that the fence posts are 4 ft 6 in to 5 ft high, so that if any extra netting is needed to stop the birds flying over you can still nail it on to the surplus part of the posts. Pig and sheep wire is very long-lasting, but it is too substantial and therefore too costly for geese, who are very rarely rough with their fencing. Also, if you have two warring ganders who must be kept apart, they can easily grip each other through such netting and do each other some harm. It is too large a gauge for goslings. Electric fencing is generally not a success either, even at 6-inch intervals from the ground.

Never use soft plastic fruit meshing for geese. It is tempting, because of price and ease of rolling up, but geese invariably get their heads, necks and even legs inextricably caught up in it, and goslings will easily strangle themselves. Rigid plastic mesh is safe, and wattle hurdles or lengths of corrugated are other, less sightly alternatives.

Rough gates can easily be made of batten (2 in × 1 in) for the simple box frame, with wire netting stapled over it, leaving spaces for hinges. Make the gates wide enough to get wheelbarrows and lawnmowers through. Hinges on the gates are definitely worth while. The tanalized posts are normally fairly straight, and give quite a good surface for fixing down the hinge.

Very small pens may be required to put a broody goose into, if you do not wish her to start sitting and incubating any eggs she may have laid. These can be made in any of the above-mentioned ways, but this time a roof will be necessary, as a determined broody goose, surprisingly, will fly out of a high-sided enclosure. A suitable size would be 5 ft × 5 ft. Such a pen, if permanently constructed, is also useful for isolating a gander or for treating an ailing bird.

Last of all, on the subject of housing and penning, it is advisable to have your housing completely ready before you bring back your birds, but only to construct two pens or paddocks to start with, as better arrangements may soon occur to you.

During hot, sunny weather geese need to drink a lot of water and must have continual access to it. In winter the demand is much less, but they still consume a lot of water. They also love swimming, and there is no doubt that swimming water encourages them to mate, although all breeds, however heavy, can mate perfectly satisfactorily without it. My largest pair of Toulouse actually prefer to mate on dry land, and do so with good results. The main objective is to try to have your watering arrangements all ready for the geese on their arrival.

If you have streams or rivers passing through your land, only very slight improvements can be suggested for such ideal watering places for geese. If the bank is steep, a wide gentle slope cut from the top of the bank down into the water will prevent leg and foot damage. Ganders will not mate if they have hurt their feet and legs, so this is worth doing. To prevent the slope becoming an unsightly mudslide, use wooden ramps (railway sleepers, perhaps) or natural flat-sided boulders firmly bedded down, or even concrete if you are going to keep a lot of geese.

Do not be depressed if your stream is very small. As long as it does not dry up in summer, it is a very hygienic method of watering stock, as the water is always being continually refreshed and the waste material washed away. It is a simple matter to build a rough stone dam across, perhaps with a piece of polythene incorporated into and against the stonework and the water flow. This would help to retain the water necessary to make a small, shallow pool, continually being refreshed. Such a pool need not be more than 3–4 ft square and 9–12 in deep to be a suitable washing and drinking place.

If your stream borders your land for some little distance, then several pools can be built at intervals; this allows each pair or trio to bathe separately from the rest. Commercial waterfowl-keepers use this system, if they have no lakes, with a series of pens running at right angles to the stream. Wire netting is taken right across the small water flow, enabling each section to have free access to it. Remember, however, not to have too many geese, for if the rate of running water is not brisk the shallow stream will soon become a stagnant ditch.

Those who have ponds or lakes only have to check on two points. Too high a number of geese will eventually foul the water, so watch your stocking rates. Secondly, cast an eye over the general field drainage into the pond, and check that septic tanks are not leaking into it. If you are in doubt, do not eat any goose eggs until you have had a micro-organism and bacteriological test done. Your local Water Authority can test water samples for a small fee. The geese themselves are unlikely to catch anything too nasty, unless the pond is really a drainage pit!

If the in-flow is very slow, deepening the water to 3 feet or so in the middle helps the excrement to settle below the level where it will be continually stirred up and drunk. Or lower the out-flow end, lowering the depth of the water, but ensuring faster drainage.

Those living in a high rainfall area will probably find that there will be other springs underground, which could add to the total in-flow of water entering the pond, and increase depth and fresh-ness. People in the west of England have employed dowsers successfully; they have miraculously found spring water, enabling them to keep waterfowl as well as obtaining a domestic water supply. These springs can have 2-inch black polythene pipes inserted at source and led down to fill special containers, or to feed a plastic-sheet lined hollow. Such dowsed springs are usually vigorous, in order to be detected in the first place, and rarely dry up; they can solve many watering problems.

Artificial ponds can be large expensively excavated ones, with the best filtering and re-circulation of the water. This is obviously the best system if you intend keeping a large flock of waterfowl. If you have more modest requirements, do not be tempted to dig out a small area for a pond unless you have given some thought to filling and draining. Setting plastic sheeting in the hollow (kept in position along the edges with bricks or rocks) works well only if the hollow tilts downhill slightly to drain away, and only if you have fresh water (through a hose, perhaps) coming in at the top end. If these two requirements are not met, the pool will soon be unhealthy, and the cleaning will prove too much.

Fibre-glass ponds, with a drainage plug in the bottom, are better. A drain-hose should be attached to the drain before setting finally in the ground, and this hose should lead downwards until it emerges on the side of a slope; the drain-hose outlet ideally should terminate outside the area belonging to the geese, so that they do not 'puddle' around in it. In order to set up such drainage, it will be seen clearly that to locate your little pond in a hollow or on flat ground is not wise. The same requirements apply to even more permanent small concrete ponds; a drainage plug and pipe must be incorporated into the cement, with the pipe leading away from the pond and slightly downhill for quick drainage.

If you intend to keep only a pair or trio, there are several methods of watering available: a hosepipe into an old farm sink or bacon-curing sink, complete with bung in the drain for easy removal and drainage; an old cast-iron bath (sunk into the side of a slope), again with drainage pipe affixed; even half a large tractor tyre, sawn with a fine blade, may suffice for a drinker. Such a tyre would not be too onerous to wash out and refill daily. Buckets can be used for just a few geese, but the limited drinking space causes fractiousness amongst the geese, especially on a hot day, and you may get tired of continually refilling them.

Old ten-gallon milk churns filled with water, turned upside down with lids on, and standing in a 15 in diameter × 3 in deep pan or bowl, is a method that works quite well. The water comes out of the ventilation holes and fills the pan until the holes are submerged. The only problem is the rather considerable weight of the full churn.

Old steel oil barrels, well cleaned out, are a good idea. An oblong horizontal cut is made through both sides of the barrel when it is lying on its side. These have the appearance of two post-box slits about 2 ft long by 8 in wide, and should be cut at a lower level than dead centre; the barrel can easily be emptied, cleaned and filled by hosepipe without a struggle.

Lastly, automatic pig-waterers are excellent for just drinking water, with a ball-cock to ensure that water is not wasted. These waterers can be moved, with hose attached, to prevent any one area of the field becoming too down-trodden; if such pig-waterers are wanted at the furthest point of the field from the water supply, large wooden or plastic barrels can be filled with water and attached to them instead, needing to be collected or refilled, when necessary, by tractor or simply by rolling them along.

However efficient these last methods may be, there is no doubt about the great pleasure derived by geese from a bathing area. Apart from keeping their plumage in good condition, water also encourages good fertility and good health.

[5]
Care and Management of Breeding Stock

Adult breeding stock is generally available for purchase in the early autumn. Adult geese are those over a year old, and which have fulfilled at least 90 per cent of their growth potential. Because of this, they will thrive on grass alone for most of the year. This is possible because good average quality, short growing grass from the spring through to late summer (in cool temperate zones) usually has a protein content of 10–14 per cent, according to which varieties of grasses form the greensward, and what weather conditions have affected it. Such levels of protein in the grass make it a sufficiently nutritious food all by itself for adult geese to thrive on outside the breeding season. This level gives a satisfactory maintenance diet, under which adult geese neither put on weight, nor lose it, and remain fit.

Nevertheless, the grazing, even in most cool temperate zones such as Britain, loses some of its protein steadily throughout the summer to early autumn. In hot and arid zones, the onset of this deterioration in the value of the grass as a foodstuff is earlier— by mid-summer in the most burnt-up areas. If the digestible protein levels drop much below 10 per cent in the grazing, even the adult geese will find it hard to maintain themselves at their current weights, and some supplementation will be required. The vitamin content of the grass also falls steeply as the grass passes its best grazing. When this stage is reached the adults will need some grain feeding, which will boost the protein and vitamin intake, but not too excessively.

As autumn comes, a twice-a-day feeding of a mixture of cereal grains, 4–6 oz per goose, during late morning, and a good handful each put in their houses at night on an old dish, will keep the protein levels acceptable at 10 per cent or a little above. Happily, it is in the autumn that the grain harvest comes in, and there will be no difficulties over supply, especially if you are growing the grain yourselves. Be careful not to feed too freshly harvested wheat all by itself. The high gluten content of new wheat tends to form a fairly indigestible mass in the gut which does no bird any good. The protein content varies most of all with wheat, but Canadian Breadwheats have 12 per cent digestible protein, while English wheats have approximately 9 per cent.

If you are supplying your own grains, they must be cleaned before feeding to geese (and other poultry) as poisonous seeds may be in the mixture; additionally, it is best not to feed grain which has been sprayed with very toxic anti-fungal or insecticidal mixtures.

Barley (9 per cent protein) should have the sharp awns removed. It is a good food for essential minerals and vitamins, and if the geese seem less than enthusiastic, rolled or crushed barley tends to go down better. Maize (6.7 per cent protein) is usually

Toulouse goose (John Hall). This goose descends from the flock bred by the late Mr Reg Appleyard, and shows a perfect keel in front.

too hard to feed whole, and for our purposes in this chapter has too high a starch and too low a protein content to be fed on its own. For feeding as part of 'mixed corn' it is broken up and called kibbled maize. Oats (8.5 per cent protein) are very fibrous, as the glumes or spikes are included in the food, and like maize ideally should not form the sole cereal for geese at this 'holding' stage of the year, although it is common practice in France.

Each of these four cereal grains found in proprietary bags of mixed corn also has a varying amount of the necessary amino-acids, vitamins and minerals, and so it seems reasonable that to feed one grain variety only may leave the geese at risk from a slight deficiency of one sort or another, as well as making for a rather boring diet. At the end of this chapter there is a chart showing the protein and carbohydrate composition of the various easily available cereals for those who may want to experiment with differing feeding regimes.

If the grazing is really bad, coming up to Christmas, and the geese are not looking as fit as you feel they should, add layers' pellets (for hens) to the corn mixture in a half and half ratio at first to see how they respond. The object in the autumn is to keep them fit, not fat or too well fed. Experiments have shown that foods with too high protein levels in the autumn achieve very little. More eggs are laid and more eggs are hatched if the higher levels of protein are fed only a month before they start laying. By making a mixture of whole grains and layers' pellets (if the grazing has completely gone) this object can be attained.

How do you tell, however, whether your grass protein levels have fallen well below 10 per cent without resorting to Ministry of Agriculture analyses? The grass must be under 4 inches long and bright, deep green, not yellow or dried or browning. It must not be dying back or coarse and seeding. The nearer to this description your grass is the higher its protein levels.

For those readers who already know in advance that there never is much available grass by mid-summer, there are some vegetable alternatives to buying 'complete' foods, such as layers' pellets. Dried grass, nuts or meal mixed in with the corn is one alternative. Dried grass nuts have a protein content of 12–16 per cent, according to which you ask for. Very good quality well-cured hay, finely chopped, is another. Maize or grass silage, cabbage leaves trimmed of their coarsest stalks, lettuces and windfall apples, potatoes and sweet potatoes will all help to boost the diet. Note from the chart, however, that although potatoes are 6.3 per cent protein they are also proportionately higher in carbohydrate (60.2 per cent) than cereals, and will have a fattening rather than a keep-fittening effect if more than a quarter of the food given is potato. Green potatoes can be used, provided that they are boiled to remove the toxin solanin, and the boiled water thrown away. Boil all potatoes fed, and add wheat bran or dried grass meal to stop the mash being too soggy for geese to relish.

Be warned that geese are excessively reluctant to accept change of any kind, and you will have to persevere in offering unusual foods to them. Do not leave these vegetable alternatives outside at night, as any frost damage will cause both protein and vitamin values to drop to nothing, apart from attracting rats and mice.

If you are farming, crops such as rye or wheat may be sown for grazing through the winter and spring if grass is non-existent, but if not enough vegetable alternatives are available then full-feeding on pellets will have to begin. Bring the birds off their bare pastures into a sloping, well-drained area or yard adjoining their house.

Construct a simple porch attached to the house to protect food and birds from any snows to come; arrange the drinkers or buckets fairly near the door of the house to try to obviate freezing up later on. Snow can be eaten if geese are desperate for water, but it lowers the eventual egg yield, as they are not enthusiastic about taking it.

If the winters are reliably severe, a small heating coil or element, thermostatically controlled, can be installed in the water container and will save a lot of bother. Ball-valve waterers are an improvement if there are quite a few geese. Running water, of course, stays unfrozen for far longer than a pond.

Lastly, before autumn is over, try to decide whether you are likely to wish you had an incubator by the spring. Often this is just the time of year when cheap, working incubators are up for sale, and these can then be bought at bargain prices. When spring comes and everyone is deluged in eggs and no broodies, and frantic to get one, the chances of buying second-hand are very slight.

Continue from autumn until the beginning of January with some grazing, plus mixed corn. With the beginning of January, it is time to consider stepping up the quality of the feed to try to get the best egg production and optimum fertility and hatching. The controversial question here is just how good a quality of food-stuff is needed?

Very little serious research has ever been focused on the goose. In Britain, the Ministry of Agriculture, Food and Fisheries state in their relevant publications that the feeding requirements of geese are by no means certain. Most goose-keepers have their own thoughts and theories as to how to do it to achieve the best results. I can speak with most authority on the best way of feeding medium to large breed geese, as I have set up over the last few years controlled groupings of Toulouse, Embdens, American Buffs and large strain Embden × Toulouse, with the help of fellow goose-rearers in this country and abroad. Better results are obtainable (for large breeds) if fed at 18–20 per cent protein for breeders. It also appears that the medium to small breeds do not respond so noticeably to any kind of dietary plan, although hatchability rather than fertility improves at these higher levels.

Many proprietary hens' layers' pellets, which have been the usual food fed to breeding geese in the absence of proper goose-breeders' pellets, are as low as 15.5 per cent protein, and are moreover very much lacking in vitamins, especially niacin (nicotinic acid) choline and biotin, as well as in minerals. Of the three above-mentioned vitamins, adult large breeds require three times as much as hens do. All three of these vitamins and most others are present in ample quantities in good, growing grass, but at the end of the year this source has declined very much. Only each individual can determine just how good or bad their pasture is, but it is likely to be as poor as 5 per cent protein at this time, well below the minimum maintenance requirement of around 10 per cent. So, just at the time you want an increase, the primary source of protein, vitamins and minerals has become almost useless.

[41]

The best solution is to feed the higher protein levels obtained from turkey breeders' pellets, where the protein content is from 18 to 20 per cent (according to individual feedstuff merchants). Pellets are preferable to mash. Experiments in Canada, the USA and Britain have shown a 20 per cent growth improvement in pellet feeding for geese, rather than with wet or dry mash. There are further drawbacks to wet mash: with at least a 5 per cent fish meal and some meat-meal content, it tends to go sour and even toxic if not eaten quickly. Dry mash sticks in the throats of geese and they do not like this, so consumption drops accordingly.

The best alternative pellets to turkey breeders are pheasant breeders (18 per cent protein) but other turkey pellet preparations are usually too highly medicated to be used without misgivings.

Aside from higher protein levels, turkey breeders' pellets have more fish, meat and liver-oils in the mixture than do ordinary hens' layers' pellets. These meals and oils provide the extra amounts of choline, biotin and niacin needed, as well as vitamins A, B_{12}, E, K and D, pantothenic acid, folic acid, and riboflavin. The increased requirements of minerals needed by breeding geese, especially the larger breeds, are calcium, phosphorus, zinc, manganese and iron, and these are also found in sufficient amounts in these pellets. Those people who have calcareous soils will, of course, present their geese with an unlimited supply of calcium without even trying! In the unlikely event that turkey and pheasant breeders' pellets are out of stock, broiler finisher pellets (19 per cent protein) are the third alternative; these have a higher level of potassium than the other two, but this does not seem to have any significance, harmful or otherwise, for breeding geese.

In spite of the nuisance of attracting wild birds, especially sparrows, I personally prefer offering 'ad-lib' feed to the geese from the beginning of the winter until the breeding season is over. This means watching very carefully throughout this period to see if there is more than just half a handful of pellets left in the troughs, when they are taken in for washing at night. If this is the case, I reduce the ration on the next day by $\frac{1}{2}$ lb. If they are hungry, however, the geese call out and come up to the house, or point nearest to it, and pace up and down. By these two expedients, it is easy to regulate matters.

Besides pellets, always leave limestone granules out for them, if your underlying bedrock is not chalk or limestone, and if the bedrock is not near to the surface. This will help form shell when the actual egg-laying begins. Geese store calcium for 15–18 days before the first egg is laid. Although good grass has an average calcium content of 10 per cent, depending on the underlying rocks, that percentage in the grass is still a minute quantity, and not sufficient to enable our domesticated geese to form shell for many eggs. Wild geese get round this problem by seeking out areas of chalk and limestone in the spring, but even so they rarely lay more than 12 eggs.

When grazing is poor and the goose cannot migrate to find calcium, she will lay the minimum number of eggs, and even these will have progressively thinner shells as she draws upon her skeletal resources. As some breeds of domestic geese rarely lay more than 30 eggs at most, this can well drop to nearly wild goose numbers if the owner does not give them access to extra supplies.

You can buy crushed oyster-shell for the adults and limestone granules for the goslings, as the latter is of smaller size. For the sake of convenience, however, it is better to buy just limestone grit for all ages. A calcium content of 0.5 per cent to 1.0 per cent is usually found in hens' layers' pellets, turkey breeders', pheasant breeders' and hens' broiler finisher pellets, but research seems to favour a higher level for geese of 2–3 per cent. (Ducks in this country receive 2.75 per cent for breeders.)

Even if the reader is keeping a large number of geese that could allow a special bulk order of goose-breeders' pellets, the inclusion of so much calcium in pellets makes it a very dusty, crumbling mixture indeed. So, in all events, placing a supply of limestone granules near to the food trough is the best way of catering for this extra need. Insoluble hen-sized grit or medium gravel should also be available, if you live in an area of good deep loam, especially, unless the geese have access to a gravel stream. Crushed flint used to be recommended, but it has been occasionally the cause of damage to the lining of the gut. The gravel or grit helps their digestive processes by breaking down the coarse or stringy fibrous grass. If there is much surface rock or stones, the birds will help themselves from the broken-up fragments.

If there are none of the aforementioned pellets available for any reason, it is possible to up-grade hens' layers' pellets to 18 per cent protein by the adding of foodstuffs to them. Soya bean meal at a 10 per cent inclusion rate, sprinkled over the pellets, is the easiest. It is readily available, as it already forms a percentage of all pellets. Soya bean meal is already 'cooked' by the supplier; the uncooked bean is toxic. It is the best balanced of any vegetable protein and is palatable for geese when added to prepared foods. It is of a comparable price per 25 K with the layers' pellets themselves.

Raising the protein level by adding fish and meat meals is also very effective, but considerably more expensive than using soya bean meal. It is advisable to keep the percentage of fish meal to below 15 per cent of the total food, as research indicates a falling off in hatchability, rather than an improvement, beyond that point, with geese. Home prepared fish and meat scraps are alternatives to bought meal. To keep costs down, however, poor grade meat or fish would have to be bought, and great care should be taken that this is not diseased or contaminated, as this would be dangerous for the preparer when cooking, and also for the geese. With care, however, this is a good method.

Dried skimmed milks and dried whey have the desired effect too, but they are very costly, even if you resort to dried milk for lambs. Nevertheless, at 27.5 per cent and 10.1 per cent protein respectively, and especially rich in minerals and vitamins, they are worth a thought if expense is no obstacle. Both are very palatable for geese. To raise layers' pellets from 15.5 per cent to 18 per cent, dried milk should form 20 per cent of whatever amount of pellets you are feeding. Liquid milk produces diarrhoea and is best given in small quantities at any stage; it is best used as a soaking agent for breadscraps. Milk, both fresh and dried, is highly digestible and a rich source of all vitamins except choline.

Dried brewers' yeast can be used for all ages of geese. At 37.4

per cent protein, it has every required mineral and vitamin for geese. Most pelleted poultry foods have a 5 per cent total inclusion of brewers' yeast anyway, but a higher proportion for waterfowl seems to be better for breeders and goslings. I give dried brewers' yeast free-choice (never fresh or raw yeast, as it can grow in the gut) by placing next to the pellet trough every morning a gallon of water, into which I pour the yeast mixture. This is made by mixing a heaped teaspoon (per gallon) of brewers' yeast with a

PROTEIN AND CARBOHYDRATE COMPOSITION OF CEREALS

Cereal	% Available carbohydrate	% Digestible protein
Barley	54.6	9.0
Maize	65.0	6.7
Oats	40.8	8.5
Brown Rice	69.8	8.4
Wheat	62.9	8.8
Wheat bran	23.0	11.1
Soya Bean meal	10.6	42.8
Milk, dried, skimmed	40.9	27.5
Grass, good, fresh or dried	5.7	12–16
Whey (dried)	53.7	10.1
Potatoes (and meal)	60.2	6.3
Brewers' yeast (dried)	13.7	37.4
Fish meal (white)	–	59.0
Liver meal	–	55.3
Meat meal	–	65.0
Eggs (hard-boiled)	–	13.7

SUGGESTED PROTEIN REQUIREMENTS FOR BREEDING GEESE

Large breeds: 18–20%
Medium breeds: 16–18%
Small breeds: 15–16%

teaspoon of sugar, and a little water in a cup until frothy. It is then stirred into the gallon bucket of drinking water. When geese are re-feathering, this yeast improves the quality of the feathers and their over-all condition. One gallon per eight large geese daily seems fine; they drink it first before turning to fresh water, so that you can be sure each goose is getting its share. It is very inexpensive to buy.

If you have very poor stock to start with, such efforts are not really necessary. Genetic strains, especially as regards size, exert a very dominant influence, and with all domestic stock the selection of the best stock, plus feeding, has been the key to successful results. It is a long process, and starting with poor stock is a setback of some magnitude. It is encouraging, however, to see what can be achieved. The Victorians took the newly-imported Embdens and Toulouse to work on, sparing no expense or trouble, encouraged by regional shows, and a general effort throughout the stockbreeding world. As a result, in 50 years, goose-breeders had achieved almost a doubling of the size and weight of both breeds. Today, in order to maintain each breed of goose at its optimum level, and prevent a regression, the same ingredients of enthusiasm, care, attention, good feeding and thoughtful selection of breeding stock are required of us as they were of the Victorians.

[6]
Hatching

When the first egg is laid in February–March the method of hatching must be decided. Some breeds of geese make excellent mothers (and fathers) at every stage of the process. Others sit for the full term, but once the first 3 or 4 goslings out of a dozen eggs are hatched they get up and go off with the first-born, leaving the remainder to go cold and die in the shell. Some sit on the eggs for 2 or 3 days, or weeks, and then suddenly decide that they will not continue. Some geese hatch off well, but have not sufficient sense to protect the goslings from rainshowers. Another problem is that geese lay every alternate day, as a rule, so it takes them about 3 weeks to have laid a dozen or so eggs, which is the optimum number for a goose to hatch off effectively.

Nevertheless, the mother very well may not go broody at a dozen. Even if she does go broody after laying 12–15 eggs, whether she hatches these out satisfactorily or not, she is unlikely to lay again that season. If however, you remove the eggs as laid, always leaving one (real or china) in the nest, she will lay on.

In my case, after I have removed what I estimate are nearly all the eggs each goose may lay a year, according to the breed norm and to my records, I do not collect for 10 days, leaving a tempting batch of about 5 eggs for each goose to sit on. Sometimes they still do not go broody, and then I take all the eggs away and pop them into the incubators I now have, in the hope that they are not too old to hatch. Sometimes the sight and feel of the eggs seems to motivate the goose, and she goes broody and will hatch off about half the eggs, on average. Once a female has

Flock of Buff Backs (Christopher Marler). This perfectly matched flock shows the buff-coloured heads, backs and thigh coverts. White feathering is usual around the beak.

'brought off' some goslings successfully, she very reliably does so every year if allowed to. The only waterfowl which is more dependable than any goose (or hen) is the Muscovy—a bird whose motherly commonsense and reliability is legendary. Many goosekeepers keep some especially for hatching eggs. For those looking for only a few goslings from their geese, however, then the mother goose herself is perfectly satisfactory; but unfortunately this is not the way to efficiency in large-scale gosling production.

The major problems with using hens are chiefly that like geese they are not always broody when you want them to be, and you have to work very hard to see that everything proceeds smoothly, so that the hen will not abandon her task. The answer to the broody question is possibly to keep a considerable number of hens, especially if you have more than 2 acres, although they can damage the greensward and spoil the quality of the grass.

[48]

If you have arranged the housing so that each pair or set of geese has their own quarters at night, then it is best to persuade the goose to make her nest in a corner of her own house. Pile lots of extra straw in the corner, and if you have a china egg put it in the middle to tempt her. If you have two females in the house, make two nests in opposite corners, and bring along a roll of 2-inch gauge wire netting, which is ready to be cut to fit from side to side across the inside of the house. This precaution may not be necessary, but it does sometimes happen that the non-broody female will try to tear up or take over the sitting female's nest. If it is going to happen at all, it usually occurs once they are shut in at night; the netting should be fixed so that each female is separated from the other, but can see and be seen.

The gander can be put in with each goose alternately at night, guided in with the long bamboo cane, until the goslings hatch, when he will be distraught if he is not with the new mother. The second female will not do any harm when all three are then put back together. Sharing the job of hatching eggs does not work out very well with geese, as their staying powers seem half as strong as usual, and the eggs are often abandoned before hatch.

If this arrangement proves unmanageable, a small pen, as mentioned in the chapter on penning, may be constructed, and a nesting shelter built on one side of the pen. Any large box or barrel will do, provided it is large enough. It does not actually need a wooden floor; the nest can be built from straw, bracken or wood chips straight on the ground in a shallow cavity dug out of the turf. To be safe, a piece of $\frac{1}{2}$-inch gauge wire netting would make an excellent fixed floor to the box; it can be pressed down into the cavity and the nest built on top. This will ensure that no vermin can enter by burrowing from underneath.

The goose ideally ought to have enough room to stand up and turn round comfortably in her temporary home. If the pen surrounding the box is built of movable weldmesh, and covered over the top as well, so that predators cannot enter, the mother goose

[49]

will be safe at night when she decides to sit on her eggs and when her young hatch, and at the same time have a little grazing and privacy from interferers by day. Put the mobile pen round her box only once she has all her eggs in the nest and refuses to come off the nest for a whole day, showing that she is broody. The pen is really for night-time protection.

Some young geese just drop their eggs in the field as they wander about. If you can pick them up before rooks, crows and magpies get them, store them in the salad compartment of the fridge until you have a goose broody and ready to accept them, when they can be placed together with any others in the nest. It is not advisable to allow a goose to make her nest in some unprotected place. Foxes know all too well about sitting geese, as do other predators. It is successful for wild geese only because they choose islands or hummocks surrounded by water for their usual nesting grounds, and avoid predators in this way.

If a goose persistently does this, and stops being broody when you try to move her nest, the only answer is to build a portable cage or house which is placed over the nest, and is heavy enough to press down well into the earth around the sitting bird. This should be made so that only one side is open to allow her to get exercise and bathe, but must be blocked securely shut at dusk, for safety. Wherever the goose sits, always put down a small amount of mixed corn and layers' pellets near the nest, with a small bucket of water. It is not often that such broodies will eat much, even though they often get very thin after a month of sitting, but they may require it.

At the end of 29–34 days, according to breed, strain and weather, the goslings will be hatched. There may be as much as 4 days between first and last hatched, depending on which eggs were laid first. The gander and the goose will probably be very fierce now, as they are anxious over the welfare of their little ones, so try not to disturb them or let children or dogs interfere with them. They will be able to take charge of the goslings, except during heavy or prolonged showers. Then you must dash out to see if the parents are going to be wise enough to lead the goslings under cover; if not you must drive them gently with the bamboo rod to their house, and shut them in if it looks as if it is going to pour all day, with food and water.

The only other provision I make is to put down a 'gosling creep' in a corner of their house, where there is little bedding. This is a simple wire netting and wood structure to fit the corner. It is raised on 8-inch legs, under which I put the goslings' chick crumbs, yeast and water. The adults cannot reach these, which is just as well, as the parents unfortunately will eat and drink everything. Gosling creeps can be employed out on the grass too, to make sure they are getting the good start in life that their owners have planned for them. Make the roof of netting so that it is not dark underneath.

An important factor in success with a broody goose is that once you have assessed the situation and decided on where and how she will be sitting set up your arrangements quickly and do not move her about any more than you can help until after the goslings are hatched. Geese need to feel secure to brood happily; if too much moved about, they may well give up the task.

Every major arrangement ought ideally to be ready by the beginning of January; construction work can be happily done in November and December when other tasks are behind. If you now consider that you might find the whole business too much trouble and would rather use an incubator after all, then place your broody in a pen with food and water, but remove all the eggs, if you have not already done so, and all of the comfortable nesting material. Leave her so that she can see the rest of the geese and they can see her, otherwise they may peck her when she is returned. Leave her there for up to 5 days. Older geese are more difficult to break of broodiness, if they have experienced motherhood, and may take the full time to lose their broodiness. See that she is safe in the pen during day and night, and after 5 days she can be returned to the others again.

SITTING HENS

If you have decided to hatch under a broody hen, check that she is really broody by placing pebbles or dummy eggs in her nest for

2 days. If she walks away, nothing is lost. If she sits it out, but you have no goose eggs as yet for her to sit on, keep her on the dummies for 2 weeks or so, in the hope that some goose-eggs will still arrive. If they do, put them under her, removing the false eggs gently at the same time. Hens (and geese) go into a kind of coma when broody; it will do no harm that she may have to sit for another month, on top of the fortnight or so, to hatch off. Keep offering grit, food and water, and do not be too alarmed if she does not eat much.

If the hen is walking or even standing, however, when the coop door is opened after 2 days, put her back with the laying hens, and wait for another to go broody. The coop can serve two purposes; that of being in use just until the baby goslings are hatched, when they may be taken away and put under a warm light or heater (a 'brooder'), or it may be used for both hatching and rearing the goslings in, for some weeks. If it is to be used in the latter capacity, it will have to be larger, weatherproof and completely safe. With this in mind I must stress the importance of making the coop rat-proof. Slatted orange boxes are not an adequate coop for a sitting hen, even when sited in a barn, unless you do not care about losing the goslings one by one as they hatch. You will be able to determine whether rats or mink have been there by the headless bodies you will find lying around, as well as by those completely missing.

Empty and sound tea-chests are admirable and cheap to buy. Tie a sheet of black plastic all round it with string, except the entrance; it will weatherproof it and help to keep out vermin too. Place the tea-chest on its side and place a flat piece of strong board over the open end for a door. A heavy brick wedged against the door will keep the broody hen and the goslings safely inside.

Such a plastic-wrapped tea-chest can be placed direct on the ground, with run-sides of weldmesh, wire netting, corrugated iron or straw bales to keep the goslings in. The hen can then come and go later on, without being able to take the goslings off very far or through long, wet grass. She will always return if she is a good broody.

While the hen is still sitting, always put grit and limestone granules down for her as well as mixed corn and water just outside the coop to help herself to. Let her out for two periods a day for an exercise. Dust the straw nesting material and also the hen herself with a safe insecticide twice during the 30 (average) days that she will be restricted there. Biting insects will drive a hen off her nest, if not dealt with. Let the hen turn the eggs herself and limit their number to 5 goose eggs, 2 if she is a bantam or a silkie.

Lastly, do not let the goslings roam outside the pen (minimum 5 ft × 5 ft) until at least 3 weeks old. So many accidents can occur to them, even with the best of hen-mothers, if they are not more or less under control. Even at 3 weeks old, it is safer simply to enlarge the pen area by adding another length of weldmesh or another bale.

Adult geese may attack goslings running with a hen, if they are free-roaming, so this is to be avoided. The adults do not realize that these are, in fact, their own children, and they can do real damage, especially to the less robust goslings.

In the case of both goose and hen, once you have the bird firmly ensconced, it is just a matter of simply waiting for the 4 weeks or so to pass. If your bird, for some obscure reason, does give up before that point is reached, and you are fairly sure that not more than an hour has passed since the nest was abandoned, such eggs may sometimes be resuscitated by transferring them either to another broody hen or into a running incubator. Eggs have been known to hatch out in airing cupboards, in pockets and even under jumpers, but in these instances there was probably only a day or so to go before the eggs were due to hatch.

Opinions still vary over whether to splash the hen or eggs (or both) with water at intervals throughout the hatch. I think this is better not done until perhaps the last 2 days before hatch. Then very warm water can be sprinkled over the eggs, rather than 'dunking' the poor hen in water, which may put her off sitting.

When the eggs start to hatch, you will usually hear tiny trillings coming from underneath the mother; she will sit exceptionally firmly now that she knows that something definite is about to happen. Try not to interfere, but if it is plain that there is going to be a gap between each hatch, owing to the various ages of the eggs as laid, then take away the first 2 or 3 goslings and put them under a lamp, or in a box on the side of a warm stove where the temperature is about 32 °C (90 °F), and hold them there until any further goslings have a chance to emerge.

If you do not do this, some hens move off the nest once there are 2 or 3 babies taking exploratory steps, and the ones in the shells will die. When all are hatched that seem likely, at night gently slip the first-born back under the hen to join their brothers and sisters. Talk softly and kindly as you do it, to reassure the hen.

Do not leave mother and newly-hatched goslings where there are other broodies, as the latter will try to take over the babies, and they may get hurt in the ensuing squabbles. Once they are hatched, goslings do not need food or water for 48 hours or so, as their last action before leaving the shell is to absorb the yolk through the umbilical cord. After 48 hours, offer fine lawn clippings or short turves, if they are not on a lawn because of inclement weather, plus chick crumbs and water in a small bowl.

Finally, as with mother geese, watch out for rain. The hen may be able to shelter her goslings when they are tiny, but not after 2 weeks or so. Goslings are susceptible to cold and pneumonia from rain, until they are feathered across their backs at 6 weeks old, and the hen will be quite unable to protect them for much of that period. Human intervention is necessary to drive them under cover.

[7]
Incubation

Once the middle of February has arrived, you may notice that the goose is looking rather puffed up around the vent area. She may also walk around the field picking up stray pieces of straw or grass, and then very carefully place these bits of straw down firmly on the ground on either side of herself. The gander will now become very protective towards her, and fierce to strangers; you will not necessarily notice the gander mating with her because geese usually choose to wait until you have left the scene. On the other hand, a very young gander may sometimes seem to have mated, having climbed on top of the goose, but it may not have been successful. Even the typical cry that ganders so often give when they seem to have mated is not always a guide, as I have seen them do this when I am quite certain no penetration had been made. All you can do is collect all the eggs, hope for the best, and remember that the eggs will probably not be fertile until at least 3 days after the first coition, and subsequent eggs may be fertile from that first mating for as many as 14–15 days afterwards.

Often the first egg is laid anywhere, and then the goose will turn to her house and build a cosy nest, where she will lay her other eggs. She will cover the eggs with the bedding material, but will not pull out very much down to line the nest until she has decided she has enough to go broody. Meanwhile, the owner must collect the eggs every morning and take them into the house for a wash and inspection. Wash with plain water (cool) and dry off carefully. Look for cracks, odd shapes and strange shell surfaces and reject all these and any other abnormalities for future incubation.

Use these rejected eggs as an extra food for the breeders, hard-boiled and chopped finely; as scrambled eggs, if not cracked, for the family; or for the dog. Once the sound typical eggs are dried, mark with an indelible marker a nought on one side of the egg, and a cross on the exact opposite side, together with a different mark for the layer, if you have more than one goose laying, and the date.

Keep a small record book and write down which goose laid and when, together with a note of the origin of any abnormal eggs. Store the eggs in a cool place; a temperature of around 4–7 °C (40–45 °F) is the best as it approximates to the range of temperature which the wild geese encounter in their normal breeding areas, and it seems to result in better hatching under incubator conditions.

A thick cloth should be placed over the eggs to keep them fairly dark. Two of the simplest suggestions for storing a few eggs are to place them in the salad compartment of the fridge, as mentioned before, or to store in a covered corn bin, buried in the grain, in a cool barn, as farmers have done for many years. Alternatively, if you have many laying geese, put the eggs on egg trays or slatted shelving (on their sides) in a cool scullery or outbuilding.

Wherever they are stored, they will need to be turned 180 ° once every day so that the contents of the egg are not allowed to stick to one place in the shell. However many laying geese you have, the best chances of good hatchings occur with eggs up to 10 days old. Although eggs do still hatch at twice this age, and especially when the goose herself is looking after them, there is a fairly steady decline in the numbers of successful incubator hatchings from 10 days onwards.

There are two main types of incubator: the still-air and the fanned-air. Both are suitable for goose egg hatching, although results indicate a very slight preference for the still-air type for very large eggs. This is because large eggs generate and retain a higher internal temperature than small eggs, and can suffer from too much constant heat particularly towards the last stages of incubation. The still-air incubator better simulates the sitting goose by giving a layered temperature, hottest at the top, coldest at the bottom. The fan-incubator, although at a slightly lower temperature, runs at an evenly hot temperature all round the eggs, leaving little chance for the larger embryo to get rid of excess internal heat as it builds up.

The temperature/humidity balance is the most crucial factor in incubation. A too high or too low temperature will cause deformities, depending on which stage of development the embryo is at. It will also change the length of incubating time. It is no good trying to correct an incubator error once it has happened. If the incubator has been running too low, running it too high for a similar period does not correct the situation. Development of the embryo goes to a set time scale, so you only compound a deficiency by over-correction, and seriously affect the vitality of the hatching goslings.

Humidity control must be such that one-fifth of the contents of the egg must evaporate during the whole period of incubation. This is the reason for 'candling' the eggs regularly throughout the incubating (see pp. 58–60), and any corrections needed can be applied as the incubation proceeds. Too much fluid in the egg will probably mean that the goslings will drown in their own fluid at hatching. Too little fluid means that the goslings will stick to the shell, or die before or at hatch. A dehydrated gosling that does manage to hatch, even with help, will be very weak and probably will not survive.

All incubators are supplied with a thermometer and it should be set so that all the readings are taken level with the tops of the eggs. Hygrometers (humidity readers) are not always supplied, but are essential for goose egg hatching. They are either (graduated in degrees) wet bulb, or percentage humidity. The manufacturer's instructions must be followed exactly, except for the levels of humidity needed for goose eggs. This is because most incubators and their instructions are devised for hatching hens' eggs. Nevertheless, the following figures have given a 70 per cent hatching of fertile eggs.

Goose eggs	*Incubation time*
large	30–34 days
medium/small	28–30 days

Ideal incubator temperature = 39 °C (101.5 °F) still air (37.5 °C [99.5 °F] fan)
Humidity throughout, until last 3 days
55% (i.e. 30/31 °C or 86/88 °F wet bulb).
Humidity last 3 days 65% (i.e. 32°C or 90 °F wet bulb).

Once the incubator has been placed in a fairly draught-free room, on a level surface, run it at the required temperature for a day at least, to see how it is working and if the temperature becomes fairly stable. Then, when satisfied that the range of temperature is not too large and all is well, place the eggs in, as directed by the instructions.

If you are going to have more batches of eggs to go in on the same shelf or into a very small single tray incubator, place a $\frac{1}{2}$-inch gauge wire netting 'box' upside down over each successive batch, so that bumping and confusion on hatch day does not damage the embryos in later batches. Likewise, if you wish to segregate goslings according to parents, these boxes, made as high as the shelf will allow, should be ready to cover and separate each strain, three days before they are due to hatch. Do not use any bulky compartment material, as the air must circulate as freely as usual.

Do not touch or even turn the eggs for the first 24 hours. Jarring bumps and shocks can so easily rupture the first tiny blood vessels forming. After the first 24 hours are over, turn the eggs, if yours is a manual machine, by hand 180 °, at least 3 times daily, or (even better) 5 times. Do not turn them an even number of times, as this will leave them on the same side throughout each long night. Obviously an auto-turn machine which turns every hour, day and night, is the very best asset.

Keep the incubator as clean as possible right from the start, to cut down contamination. Egg shells are very porous, and once infection sets in it can ruin a whole hatch. Fumigate at the end of each hatch if possible.

On the 7th to 9th day 'candle' the eggs for fertility. This is best done in a darkened room with a powerful torch held under the egg, or with a home-made or bought 'candler'. An old brandy bottle box, with an electric light bulb attached to a cable and plug, makes a very effective candler. Cut out on one side of the box, and at the furthest end from the opening, a slightly smaller shape of an egg than you would be expecting to be incubating. You can line that end with reflective silver foil so that when the light bulb is placed in the box and switched on, the intense light shines up through the egg-shaped hole and shows up the contents of the egg, which is placed on top of the hole.

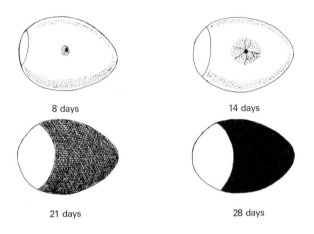

8 days

14 days

21 days

28 days

Stages of development in an incubating egg.

If the egg is fertile, there will be at the very least a very small dense black dot, about match-head size, and, if robustly fertile, a fine network of spidery web-like veins radiating out from the dot. The whole will move about in the egg if it is most gently rotated, but be very careful not to move jerkily.

If you are not positive whether you saw a dot or not, leave for a further 5 days and then re-candle. If there is definitely no sign of any dot, however small, these are infertiles or 'clears', and should be removed from the incubator. Where you have many batches of eggs in the incubator, close the door while you examine a complete batch, so that no damage is done to those eggs inside by a drop in temperature.

After 7 days of incubation, spray the eggs quickly in the morning, with a fine spray bottle full of cold water, up to the last 3 days, then stop. Watch the ventilation control as the humidity temporarily leaps up. Apart from an attempt to copy the sitting goose, who may take a quick bathe, leaving the eggs for a while and then returning cold and wet from her swim, the early morning spray gives them a chance to cool down and not over-heat.

By the 14th to 15th day, if the eggs are fertile, and the embryos still alive since the last candle, the whole vein pattern will be much larger and darker, with a more decided line, showing the beginning of the air sac, like an aura. This air-sac will and should be enlarging. If there is no air sac to be seen, the embryo has died, and the egg will slowly go rotten, so it must be removed at once in case it explodes later, and ruins the hatch and the germ-free incubator.

On the 21st to 22nd day, the dark area should fill most of the shell up to the air sac, and the air sac should have increased its size once again. Do not turn in the last 3 days or otherwise disturb. If the hatching eggs are to be transferred to a 'hatching' incubator, do it at the start of the last 3-day period and very gently, having set up and run the hatcher for at least 2 days previously, so that the eggs are transferred straight into the right constant temperature and humidity. In these last 3 days, the gosling needs to get himself ready with his head under his wing, in order to peck his way out through the membrane into the air sac for his first breath, and then out through the shell. Moving him at this last stage can frustrate his efforts, and he may become too tired trying to get himself correctly placed, if someone has turned him upside down!

As this last stage approaches, the temperature of the machine will gradually have to be turned down, as the embryo starts generating its own heat as its metabolic rate increases. This happens to a greater degree with large eggs, and the temperature must be correctly kept. Ventilation is a necessity at all times, and ventilation holes should never be covered completely, as it is quite possible to kill embryos by oxygen starvation.

If with some of the small older-type incubators you cannot get the humidity high enough, stand a jamjar of water in the corner of the tray, and place a sponge in it, so that it protrudes from the water for a couple of inches. This achieves an immediate rise in humidity to the required level. With the temperature and humidity running at the right levels, on the appropriate day cheeping sounds will be heard from some eggs, accompanied by the rocking of certain ones. Do not despair if you can detect neither sound nor movement from other eggs.

The goslings will first get into the air sac, and then may have a complete rest for any time up to 24 hours. Then they will punch a hole or crack through the shell itself, followed by further rest. Only after this will they start 'rimming', or punching a half-circle shape round the air sac end of the shell. Cross-bred goslings go through all these stages much faster than pure-bred ones.

Unless it can be clearly seen that a gosling has its beak completely stuck through the shell and cannot even open its mouth, do not help by enlarging the hole for him. Often he is not ready to come out; he may be ingesting his egg yolk through his navel, and by enlarging too soon the rush of air inside the shell will dry out the fine skin of the yolk, making it leathery. The gosling will not then be able to take it in and re-absorb it, and will die. Often such helpful human efforts cause blood to appear round the shell; if this should occur, stop at once. If he is going to hatch at all, the blood vessels should have dried up and there should not be fresh blood anywhere.

The only case in which intervention is acceptable is when a piece of membrane or shell gets stuck over the gosling's nostrils, though he is otherwise freeing himself quite well. The removal of the piece with tweezers does help.

The first gosling may be out as much as 3 or 4 days before the final one, but normally there is a 2-day gap. If the final egg is still bobbling about after all the others have hatched, candle the egg very quickly to see if you can see his beak protruding into the air sac. If not, then a satisfactory outcome is unlikely. If the beak is protruding, however, at the end of 2 days after his family hatched you can make a small hole at the air sac end of the shell to help. A screw is the best instrument to use, leaving a match-head size aperture. Even so, the delay is not infrequently caused by a leg deformity, in which case the leg will not go into the right position to help in the pushing out of the shell, so try, by all means, but be philosphical over the outcome.

Once the hatch seems as complete as it is going to be, they can be left in the incubator without food and water for at least 48 hours. If you have other batches on the same shelf, however, it is worth taking them out to put them under the heat lamp or artificial brooder.

[8]
Care and Feeding of Goslings and Young Geese

Goslings are basically very affectionate, trusting and contented, and not nearly as apprehensive as ducklings. The only onerous chore is that of keeping them on spring grass and yet dry at the same time. For this reason I would wholeheartedly advise the beginner to try to arrange for the first hatches to be later rather than earlier in the year, if at all possible. Ideally, the beginner in cool temperate zones such as the British Isles should try to arrange the first batch to arrive in April rather than March, even if it means eating the first laid eggs. The simplest way of achieving this, especially in the more northerly areas, is to hold back feeding the breeders their really good diet until February has arrived. (Early good feeding tends to advance the start of laying and also the hatching.) If this is done, it improves the chances of early grass, warmer weather, and fewer really chilling showers to harm baby goslings.

Once the goslings are ready to leave the incubator, no later than 72 hours old, they are ready to be sexed and marked. It is easiest to sex goslings at 1 or 2 days old rather than later on, and methods of doing this are clearly explained in Chapter 9.

There are four ways in which they can be housed: firstly, under or in a specially manufactured 'brooder', suitable for baby chicks, where goslings will have adequate room for 2 or 3 weeks; secondly, in a small hen house connected to the electricity supply and near the house, for your own convenience; thirdly, in a section of a larger building, but with plenty of allowance made for the draughtiness of such a place; fourthly, in a very large cardboard box in your warm kitchen.

Four-week-old goslings. The two goslings with dark fluffy down, and nearly black beaks, are Toulouse. This colour changes to pale orange at 3 months. The rest are Embdens.

With not more than 10 goslings in each batch, I would advise keeping them in the large cardboard box in the kitchen for their first week. This is mostly because, with small numbers, should the electricity supply fail in the night, or the weather turn bitterly cold, there are not enough of them to generate sufficient body heat to keep all of them alive, if they are in an outside building. What happens in such a situation is that the smaller females or any less robust goslings try to push into the centre of the huddle to warm up, but are pushed out by the bigger ones, and become chilled and die. With this method you can also keep an eye on general progress while you are busy indoors during the day. During that first week, spraddled legs will be obvious if the goslings are at hand, and can be dealt with at once by placing a rubber band firmly round the top of both legs above the joints. Any sickly goslings can be removed and placed in another box until it can be seen whether they are going to improve or not, thus preventing any possible infection spreading to them all.

The box itself can be burnt after each hatch if necessary, to keep everything completely fresh and sanitary. The best boxes are those used to pack televisions, fridges and rolls of fabric, as these have high draught-excluding sides. Line the bottom with plastic sheeting, and then put in a 5-inch thick layer of wood chips. Sawdust is nearly as good, but occasionally goslings eat the sawdust, presumably in mistake for chick crumbs, and so it is not my first choice. At intervals, the very topmost layer of dirty chippings can easily be removed and burnt, and a fresh layer put on top. At the end of 3 weeks' use, throw all the woodchips away and start completely afresh. Straw is not absorbent enough, and also trips up their wobbly legs as they try to take their first steps.

Place a shallow tray in the food corner, just large enough to put a small bowl of crumbs and small bowls of yeast and water on. Make sure the sides of the tray are not more than ½ inch high, as the goslings will not be able to get over the edges to feed. Put a large stone, or small upturned terracotta flower pot, in the centre of the water bowl, to prevent the goslings from climbing in and getting soaked or even drowned.

From a socket near at hand, put together a plug and lead and fix either a 250 watt infra-red bulb or a 200 watt ordinary light bulb in a bulb-holder at the other end of the cable. Either a special bright aluminium shade from poultry equipment suppliers may be fixed over the bulb-end, or a home-made shade can be cheaply assembled. A bare wire lampshade-maker's frame, covered with aluminium foil bright side innermost, makes the cheapest reflector of all.

Fix the lamp so that it hangs over the centre of the box. Infrared bulbs do not need a shade; one bulb for every 50 goslings is usually adequate. They work differently from light bulbs in that infra-red energy does not become heat until it is absorbed.

The temperature of the floor area underneath the lamp should be at 32 °C (90 °F) for the first week, 27 °C (80 °F) the second week, 21 °C (70 °F) the third week, and if the weather is quite reasonable it may be possible to switch off during the day-time at least, especially in summer. Keep on at nights for longer, but keep raising the level of the lamp gently week by week until you are certain the nights are not cold.

If you use electric light bulbs, starting with 200 or 150 watt and finishing with 60 watt at nights at 4 weeks, their eating period is extended to 24 hours, and it helps to build a bigger goose. This is the method, but on an enormous scale, used by the Polish in their table-bird production.

The best guide to whether the goslings, however many you have underneath, are warm enough is to see how they sit. If they are huddled tightly together and trying to work their way to the centre of the group, it is far too cold. If they are spread out nicely underneath, peacefully and in small separate groups, then the temperature is right.

When night comes, lower the cable and light down just an inch or so from this correct daytime level, as nights are colder. Any kind of tripod or trestle that can stand either in or over the box is an ideal place to fix the cable, and makes it easier to raise or lower the lamp.

If, however, the family have a rooted objection to rearing the goslings for a week actually in the kitchen, then resort must be made to the other outside housing. Make sure that whichever building the brooder-lamp is going to be set up in is completely mouse- and rat-proof. Rats are murderous, but even mice can contaminate the goslings' food, and in their first week they have not the sort of resistance to such rodent-born infections as they will have at 3 weeks old. It may be necessary to start them off in a specially adapted building outside, if you are hatching large batches.

The need for an electricity supply to whatever out-house you will be using is essential. The same arrangement of hanging heat or light bulbs must be set up in advance, with a plentiful thickness of wood chippings, just as in the kitchen, except if you have many goslings, when proper chick waterers and troughs will have to be bought. Straight-sided troughs save some food wastage. Water containers should allow the goslings to submerge their beaks past their eyes, if at all possible, otherwise their eyes can become sticky and sore.

Very much will depend on the weather as to whether it is warm enough in their first week to put them out onto the grass. If it is warm, they can be taken in a carrying box to specially prepared nursery pens for a few hours in the sunniest part of the day. As mentioned in the penning section, keep these nursery pens very close to the house, so that rooks, magpies and crows do not come to attack the goslings.

When they are only to be out for an hour or so because they must not get chilled, there is no need to move their chick crumbs or brewers' yeast out with them. Just take their water bowl; they will be so pleased to be eating the short fresh grass that they will hardly touch the crumbs. It they are to be out for longer than 2 hours, take the chick crumbs along.

The fewer the goslings, the shorter the time must they be left without checking up on them. Remember that they would normally turn to the mother goose periodically for warmth, but now they only have their own combined body heat to fall back on. If they are peeping sadly and very huddled, bring them in at once to their kitchen or out-building home, where the light should have been left on to keep the bedding warmly welcoming.

When the weather is bitter, it is advisable to keep them in their box for the first week, or longer if need be. Grass can be brought to the goslings, instead of the goslings going to the grass. Short lawn clippings, fresh every day, about $\frac{1}{2}$ inch in length, placed in a bowl or dish, are just as good. Alternatively, to give goslings that necessary physical exercise of pulling with beak and neck, cut turves from a suitably short grassed area, about 1 foot long by 6 inches wide. Placed in the nursery box, on a small plastic bag to stop them dampening the wood chips, the earth still attached, they keep fresh for quite a long time.

When the very worst situation arises, and there is endless snow, dried grass meal or dried grass nuts at 16 per cent protein are the only really feasible alternatives to fresh grass. If in nut-form, crush the nuts in a cotton bag with a hammer and sprinkle the chick crumbs with it to a total of about 5 per cent of all the food. They do not enjoy it as much as fresh grass, but there may not be a choice.

[67]

By the time the week-old goslings are ready to go out to their heated house, they should already have started off well, nutritionally, and be growing rapidly. They should also be able to survive a minor accident or infection. Make sure that their new quarters have wood chippings on the floor, not flat newspapers or bare boards. These would give a gosling no toe-holds, and his legs may become spraddled through slipping about. The best small house should open its doors on to an area of short, mowed grass, not soiled by adult geese, within the larger nursery paddock. Use weldmesh tied in sections with string to form a small square pen outside the house door. This will limit the extent to which they can move away from the house and its warm lamp. A shallow ramp, preferably with sides, can lead from the house to the ground. As the goslings grow, the weldmesh can have further sections added to increase the area, until it can be dispensed with altogether, and the goslings can have the full use of the whole nursery pen.

When the spring and early summer are proving to be exceptionally wet, it is best, in the long run, to buy clear strengthened plastic sheeting to tie down over the top of the weldmesh pen. This is easily done, and it allows the warmth of the sun to penetrate but not the rain. It also reduces those numerous excursions you would have had to make to push them into their house to keep dry. An investment in clear sheeting or heavy duty polythene is a really good one, if you intend to rear goslings each year. If the season proves very hot and dry, the plastic has its uses as a sunshade. Put the goslings' food, water, yeast mixture and limestone granules near the door of the house, so that they can feel the warmth coming from the lamp inside.

Do not allow the goslings to swim yet. Leave that until they are at least feathered a little underneath their bodies, unless the mother goose is rearing them. Keep their quarters as clean as possible. When they are put indoors at evening time, put the bowls of food and clean water in with them, if you are aiming for their greatest potential growth rate. They will eat in the late evening and at dawn if food is available, and gain weight rather faster this way. The only thing to watch out for is mouldy food, which

Trio of exhibition American Toulouse (Christopher Marler). This fine trio shows the large convoluted gullet or dewlap, loose feathering, full deep keel and large paunch required by breed standards.

may cause aspergillosis. Clean out their quarters more frequently, perhaps weekly, if food is going in with them.

Once they are seen to be getting too big for their quarters, they must progress to larger housing. Outside in the nursery area, try to rotate the use of the grassy pens, giving each pen a chance to recover and grow after the goslings have been moved from it. This will also mean that the goslings are always grazing on clean fresh grass. When you notice the grass in their pens being eaten right down low, at the end of the day, enlarge their grazing area again.

Dried brewers' yeast for all breeds throughout a good part of the year is again to be recommended. I feed it whenever I am doubtful over the quality of either the grass or the prepared food-stuffs. I make the mixture up as for the breeders, except that I do not make it in gallon lots. I use more dried brewers' yeast for the goslings per amount of water; about half a teaspoon of yeast for every pint of water, with half a teaspoon of sugar. Experiments and research have shown that the inclusion of brewers' yeast in a poultry diet promotes growth improvement. The Ministries of Agriculture in Britain and the USA have discovered that it can give as much as 20 per cent growth improvement for waterfowl, if the quantity included in the diet is raised to 5–10 per cent. It certainly seems to increase the appetite in both upland and water-fowl.

Large breed goslings have a higher requirement of all dietary ingredients than small breeds, so the amount of brewers' yeast in chick crumbs needs to be boosted to suit their requirements. The 10 per cent level is about right for them. Experiments have shown that groups of goslings fed on brewers' yeast from hatching until 4 months of age are noticeably broader and bigger than those which were not fed in this way.

Most experienced goose-rearers are agreed on at least one point. Goslings need to be started off on a nutritious diet if they are to do well. The controversial questions are how high a level of protein to feed and for how long? There are two schools of thought on the matter. The first is to feed chick crumbs at around 18 per cent protein to all sizes of breeds, until the goslings are about 4 weeks old, then switch them to growers' pellets at about 16 per cent for another 4 weeks. At 8 weeks old they are then put onto wheat, rolled barley or mixed corn. This regime is a lower protein one and intends the goslings to be given constant access to grass from their first week, as does the second school of thought on the subject.

This second method is to feed the above dietary levels to small and medium breeds, but to increase the protein levels for the larger breeds to 20 per cent. The goslings may be kept at 20 per cent protein from hatch to 3 weeks old, dropping down to 18 per cent until 8 weeks or longer. At 8 weeks old or so, they are put on growers' pellets until 16 weeks old, from which time onwards they are given wheat or rolled barley.

Neither method has actually proved to be the most effective way of rearing for size or health, and the whole problem is, in any case, dependent on how good a strain of goose you are experimenting with. It must also be remembered that all these levels of proteins, minerals and vitamins will be considerably diluted and reduced if the goslings are on poor quality grazing, as is often the case in the early spring. Likewise, if the grass is at its highest level of 16 per cent protein, there will be less need to feed rich prepared foodstuffs.

On balance, though, for large breeds such as Toulouse and Embdens, a 20 per cent level to start off with may be best, as it gives the goslings a higher proportion of minerals, vitamins and protein for body-building, but it is important only to keep them at this level for 3 weeks, as slow-developing birds should not be 'forced' too quickly in case slipped wings or leg weaknesses develop.

There may be a case for dispensing with growers' pellets at 8 weeks of age and feeding boiled wheat with perhaps dried skimmed milk added, to keep the protein, minerals and vitamins at a higher level than just wheat alone.

Below are suggested levels of protein, suited to each category of breed, for gosling feed, but none of these suggestions is immutable.

Breed	0–3 weeks with grass	4–8 weeks	8–16 weeks	16 weeks+
Large	18–20% chick crumbs	18% chick crumbs	16% growers	12% grain
Medium	18% chick crumbs	16% growers	12% grain	12% grain
Small	18% chick crumbs	16% growers	12% grain	12% grain

It will be noticed that to feed large breeds a 20 per cent protein diet, the chick crumbs will need other foodstuffs added, to raise the total level up from 18 per cent. If this higher protein feeding regime is going to be followed, there are some valuable foods that can be used to do it. Best suited to goose requirements are fish or meat meals. If 5 per cent is added to each feed of chick crumbs, the protein level will rise to 20 per cent. Soya bean meal (see Chapter 5) is another valuable addition, as is dried skimmed milk. If either are added to the feed to the extent of 20 per cent of the whole amount, the chick crumbs will be boosted to 20 per cent protein.

A cheap but valuable source of additional minerals and vitamins, regardless of whether you decide to use the lower or higher protein diet for your goslings, are the hard-boiled eggs which come from the incubator as infertiles. As a goose egg is 13.7 per cent protein only, it has a slightly lowering effect on the total protein content of chick crumbs, rather than raising it, but this is counteracted by the over-all nutritional value of the egg. Chop the egg finely, and add to the crumbs. To avoid making the goslings constipated, do not add more than one goose egg to every 2 lb of crumbs.

Hard-boiling is better than mixing in raw. Raw albumen contains a trypsin inhibitor which reduces the digestibility of the egg. If it is cooked, 86 per cent is totally digestible. The fact that these infertiles have been in the incubator for 7 days or so does not impair the food value. The two vitamins, biotin and choline, which are needed in double the quantities in goslings than in chicks, are also present in the eggs, but again the biotin is only available to the gosling after cooking. These factors, combined with that of a high vitamin B_{12} content, which is known to promote good growth, make the egg magnificent food for growing baby geese.

Dried milks, or liquid goats' milk, can also be added to crumbs with the same beneficial effects as in adding brewers' yeast, but do not leave a dampened mixture longer than one day, in case it goes sour.

If you are providing such foods as ad-lib fortified chick crumbs, plus dried brewers' yeast, fresh water, and limestone granules to provide for the extra calcium need to build good, strong, large frames, you need not worry about not having any grass for your goslings. You are providing a complete feed, and can just wait patiently for the warm days and new grass to arrive. Once the spring growth has begun, the goslings will increase their grass consumption and lower their intake of prepared foods.

Under certain circumstances, it is possible to rear goslings on grass alone. Firstly, as previously mentioned, the smaller the breed or strain, the less their requirements. Secondly, so much depends on when the goslings are hatched. If they are hatched towards summer when the grass is at its very best, perhaps even 16 per cent protein, the smaller breeds, who are not much bigger than their wild relatives, will find the grass alone an adequate diet. There definitely seems less point to better feeding of the small breeds, or even small strains of medium breeds, as they seem to eat as much, or more, food as large breed geese but metabolize it very differently.

Medium to large breed goslings will not find grass alone to be adequate, and cannot be expected to fulfil their potential growth on a grass diet only. As it is, it is only for a very brief period that such a high peak-level of protein in the grass can be expected. If goslings are reared on grass only, at somewhat below this protein level, they will not do well at all.

Most breeds put on at least three-quarters of their eventual adult weight in their first 4–5 months of life, with the highest percentage rate of gain in the first weeks. Small breeds make the largest percentage rate of gain up to 3 weeks old; medium breeds to 8 weeks old; and large breeds to 12 weeks old.

The rate of growth of Embdens in their first 12 weeks, for example, when really well fed, is impressive. Their weight doubles every week until 4 weeks, and then slows to about 3 lb a week until about 10 weeks old, when it drops to about 1 lb weekly up to 9 months old.

Toulouse are rather strange as they start off as smaller goslings from smaller eggs than Embdens, and do not gain so dramatically. They have made just two-thirds of their eventual bodyweight by 20 weeks old, but they continue slowly growing and thickening up until they are about 18 months or more, according to strain. For small and medium breeds, the rate of growth is such that by 5 months of age they hardly put on another ½ lb of weight unless closely confined and fattened. Even so, this puts extra fat on the bird, not the lean meat that the buyer is more likely to prefer.

Because gosling growth rate is at its greatest before they are 4 months old and after that falls away rapidly for all but Toulouse (and to a lesser extent Embdens), this is not only the best, but the only time to build sound, large frames and big meaty bodies. To scrimp and economize at this time is 'penny wise and pound foolish'. When the growth rate has slowed down to almost nothing, then economies can be made by stopping the prepared foods, and putting the young geese on to grass only, during the day, with cheaper mixed corn in the evenings.

Although it is rather frightening to contemplate ad-lib feeding from a cost point of view, in fact, if the grass is good and they have nearly fulfilled all their potential growth, their consumption of the prepared foodstuffs falls away rapidly, so it is often not as expensive a method as might be feared.

About $\frac{1}{4}$ lb of mixed corn or wheat will be the right amount for each young bird to go to bed with. There is no need to put water containers in the houses once they are over 3 months old, unless there is a high proportion of oats and barley in the feed, or unless they are being given all the day's food allowance in their houses at night.

Once the young geese are ready to go onto grass alone during the day, they can stay on grass either until you want to kill them for the 'green goose' trade at Michaelmas, or until the Christmas fattening period begins.

PRACTICAL HOME-PREPARED STARTING RATIONS FOR MEDIUM AND LARGE BREED GEESE

Ingredients	Starting (lb)	Growing (lb)	Breeding (lb)
Ground maize (corn)	25	30	25
Ground wheat	15	15	15
Ground barley	15	15	10
Ground oats	10	5	5
Wheat bran	–	–	5
Soybean oil meal	15	15	20
Fish meal	10	10	8
Dehydrated green feed	5	5	5
Dried brewers' yeast	5	5	5
Bone meal	–	–	1
Ground oyster shell	1	1	$1\frac{1}{2}$
Cod liver oil	1 oz	1 oz	1 oz
Iodized salt	$\frac{1}{4}$ oz	$\frac{1}{4}$ oz	$\frac{1}{2}$ oz
Wheat germ oil	–	–	4 oz

[9]
Sex Determination and Marking

The only geese which are auto-sexed at hatch are Pilgrims and West of Englands; ganders are yellow at hatch and later become white, geese are greyish green and become grey with some white on head and neck, and often on their backs too. Embdens are the next easiest to sex at hatch, because usually, but not always, the females have darker fluff across their backs than males. Other breeds of geese are next to impossible to sort successfully into males and females from their appearance at hatch or even into adulthood. Chinas and Russian Kholmogorsk can be visually sexed at about 6–8 months old, when the knobs on the ganders are noticeably larger than those of the females, and the ganders are quite considerably larger in appearance.

Some strains of Toulouse have very shortnecked females; but in other strains their necks are as long as the ganders. The owner of geese can watch carefully nonetheless (bearing in mind the likelihood of mistakes) for larger, coarser feet and legs, heavier bodyweight, bigger heads, possibly longer necks, a more aggressive manner towards other geese at the food trough, or towards dogs and strangers, and a louder, shriller calling voice. These may be ganders. Ganders also tend to hiss rather more than geese, but not always, so the only real answer to the problem is to give each bird a ventral examination.

The best times to do this are at hatch, before the goslings have taken in any food, or at 7–8 months old. At hatch the baby gosling is easy to hold in one hand, while gently exploring the ventral area with the fingers of the other hand, and there is less

Flock of Brown Chinas (John Hall). The slim and elegant build of this particular breed is an important requirement. Underlines should be completely free of both keel and paunch.

likelihood of the operation becoming messy if they have not eaten first.

At 7–8 months onwards, geese are acquiring full adulthood, and the sexual organ in the gander is too pronounced to be mistaken. Moreover the muscular control around the vent relaxes under manipulation when adulthood is reached, but does not do so at all readily before that stage.

The most satisfactory way of sexing any adult age of goose is to use a table top upon which to place the bird, on its back and with its tail half over the edge of the table, and unsupported. To sex geese by placing them upside down between the knees is the usual method practised by experts, but this can prove difficult in stubborn cases.

An assistant will be needed to hold down the bird on the table.

Press the tail end and vent downwards over the end of the table, and, with finger and thumb on either side of the vent, very gently press in towards the body of the goose, opening the lips of the vent and then closing alternately as you press. Repeat this opening and shutting several times, while pressing into the body of the goose slightly. Do not under any circumstances be rough, which could damage the bird, and also the pain of such rough handling will cause the muscles round the vent to contract tightly. The object is to persuade the muscles to relax and open, and it is better to continue for a longer period gently than to become impatient.

Note closely while you are alternating this movement whether the vent is slightly prominent, convex, firm to the touch and looking smoothly conical when closed. If there is a general pale pink colouring of this vent when closed and also when partially open (even if no penis is actually visible) the whole of the above factors mentioned point to the bird being a gander.

A female vent opens with far less manipulation; is and feels slightly concave; is markedly more wrinkled from the outside; and when viewed on the inside is much darker in its pink colouring than on the outside. The whole ventral area has a softer, more wrinkled, recessed feel under the fingers than in the case of a gander.

None of these manipulations are easy to begin with, but persevere, and try to sex several geese, so as to notice the contrast between the two sexes. If all goes very well, the penis in a gander will protrude through the vent. It will be 2–4 inches long at 8 months, according to breed, palest pink and markedly spiral.

If, however, you would prefer to sex the goslings at hatch or under a week old, hold the baby upside down in your hand with its head towards your body. Slide your forefinger under the tail end, opposite to the vent on the top side. This will raise the ventral area upwards. With the index finger of the same hand, hold down the very edge of the tail. With your other hand, press down the tail end towards the ground, so that it is nearly at right angles to its body. Begin very gently to manipulate the ventral opening as in adult geese, and repeat several times until the muscles relax somewhat.

If it is a gander, there will be extra tightness, a conical hardness of the closed vent, and the very palest pink exterior and interior to it. If you can get the vent to open really well, a baby gander will have a small $\frac{1}{8}$-inch rounded penis, like a minute finger, lying just inside the central opening. A female will be more concave around the closed vent, slightly darker pink and wrinkled inside, with lumps and ridges internally, but with nothing so positive as the penis of the baby gander.

Obviously it is advisable to sex at hatch, as it may be that you have all ganders and may not want to be at the expense of rearing so many ganders, unless your speciality is the Christmas meat trade. You will also find it convenient if you know from the start how many of each sex you have available for sale to your customers.

Once this sexing at hatch has been mastered, marking the birds can now take place. If you have carefully segregated each strain whilst in the incubators, you will want to mark on each gosling its sex and its strain, and record this in your notebook. There are three main methods of marking birds: the first is to punch or cut into the webs of the feet; the second to fix wing bands; and the third to put rings on the legs.

On a baby gosling's foot, each of the two webs give enough area to punch two small holes in each, with a sharp leather punch. Once the sex of the goslings has been decided, the owner can determine which web on which foot the sex of the young will always be punched. For example, females can go unmarked, but ganders can have one punch hole made in the inner web of the left foot of the bird.

The other spaces may be used for strains; one punch hole to denote strain A, two holes to denote strain B, on the inner webs of the right legs, or whatever the owner prefers. Beyond that, strains will need to be marked with small leg rings in different colours (being careful to change these rings for larger sizes until full adult size is reached) as too many punch holes in tiny webs are obviously not desirable. The size usually required for goslings at hatch is about $\frac{3}{8}$-inch internal diameter, while large breed ganders often require 1-inch internal diameter in special turkey stag sizes. With so many variations of sizes between strains as well as breeds, it is best if each owner measures, with a piece of narrow tape, the best size to suit their own geese, and then sticks to the same supplier, if satisfied, for each year's replacement rings. Flat band cellulose or plastic rings are fine for goslings up to 2 months old, but hopeless after that age. They quickly pull them off from that age onwards, and 2, 3 or 4 coil spiral rings are best from then on. Poultry equipment merchants will be able to supply, or special advertisements in poultry-keeping magazines will help you obtain them.

Aluminium rings are available, with numbers. These can be used to denote the sequence in which each gosling hatched. So much is personal preference. Wing bands are quite good, but are not often used, as they do not show at all when the bird is walking about, and so it has to be caught and examined.

Some people cut wedges out of the goslings' outer webs, or along the leading front edges of the main webs. The wedges rarely stay easily recognizable by adulthood, however, and cutting into the front leading edges can cause the web to split up towards the ankle, if the foot is placed awkwardly over a stump or stone. Certainly if any cutting or punching of holes is to be done, it should humanely be accomplished before the goslings are more than 3 days old, otherwise excessive bleeding may occur, and infection set in. Graded rings do have an advantage over these surgical marking methods, in that should the sex be determined wrongly rings can be altered, but punch holes and cuts cannot.

[10]
Grassland Management

Geese are natural grazers, and, whatever prepared grain foods are fed to them, it is best for their general health and happiness if at least a part of their food intake consists of grass. Under domestication, geese are usually given a very limited range upon which to graze, and therefore it is up to their owner to see that their range is as good as it can be, for the health of the birds, and to save some of the expense of bought feed. Too many goose-keepers just pitch them on to scrubby old patches of worn-out pasture, and expect them to prosper. They cannot.

On the other hand, many people have lawns and grassy orchards which are absolutely suitable for geese, but the idea of lawn-mowing with geese does not occur to them. As mentioned in an earlier chapter, 10–15 heavy breed and 20 light breed geese can be kept on one acre, especially if that acre is good, lush grass, not liable to brown and dry up in summer or become overrun with nettles and docks. Such stocking rates on an acre will certainly leave the greensward like a billiard table at the end of the winter and before the new spring growth, but it is still feasible without reducing the field to a bare barren patch.

Taking into account, however, the vagaries of the weather, and allowing for an exceptionally hot, dry summer, it would be wiser to reduce these 'ideal' rates somewhat. Then again, if you intend to rear goslings from your adult birds, take into account that one-third of the area will be needed for the youngsters from spring until they are sold. A further reduction of the numbers of adults may be better. You are lucky if you have plenty of land.

Nevertheless, an acre of excellent grass, well looked after, is as nutritionally valuable as 3 acres of poor grass. Weed control is the first objective. Some so-called weeds found in pasture are not pervasive, and do not slowly blot out and take over the sward; but even so, weeds in general are nutritionally useless. Some of the worst weeds, such as docks, plantains and nettles, are not only grass-excluding but are never eaten by geese, under any circumstances, and so will go on to seed and spread unchecked unless action is taken.

There are five possible courses of action, varying in effectiveness. Firstly, they can be dug up with a trowel or special dock-lifting tool. This is limited in its success, as with docks and plantains only the tiniest roots have to be left in the soil to enable the plant to re-establish itself. It works well with nettles and other tall stringy weeds.

Secondly, docks can be systematically clipped with long-handled shears. This is surprisingly effective, but laborious, as you have to keep on and on cutting the leaves, as they grow, at fortnightly intervals or so. It is best done in the spring, when the docks are undeniably discouraged by the treatment. The grass then has a chance to form a light-excluding mat over the head of the docks. Long-handled shearing is useless with rosette-type weeds like plantains.

Thirdly, Weedol or similar 'kill all' mixtures can be used on densely weed-infested areas with such as ground elder or even couch grass. Couch grass is not very nutritious and is not a favourite with any grazing animal. These mixtures are not so successful with docks, but very successful with plantains, especially if the mixture is applied from a light back-pack sprayer and is used in a 'spot' spraying way, avoiding the surrounding grass. Where Weedol (and other paraquat-containing preparations) has been used all over an area, the geese must not be allowed to graze or walk over it for 3 weeks following treatment, hence another use for weldmesh penning. If it has been 'spot' sprayed, and the surrounding grass is of good quality, so that there is plenty for the geese to eat, then there is only the need for the geese to be kept off until the first heavy shower of rain following the spraying.

The plantains, in particular, brown and wither very quickly, and the grass rapidly takes over.

Fourthly, and the best method, I believe, is to use weed-killers which leave the grass unharmed. 'Spot' spraying of these preparations is best, unless there are many weeds per square yard; in this case pen the geese out. A liquid is far better than a scattered powder, as it is absorbed by the foliage almost immediately and need not be applied in a blanket-type method, which I consider dangerous for grazing animals of any kind, if they are to remain on the treated pasture.

The effect of these weed-only killers, which usually contain the chemicals 2,4-D and Mecoprop, is not dramatic at first. During the week following application, nothing at all seems to be happening, then dock and plantain appear to be writhing and, if anything, growing apace. Despite this, in the next two weeks these plants are either dying back or can be cut back, as the root is killed anyway. If you cut back, rake up the dying leaves and stalks, and dispose of them away from the geese. Always follow the instructions of such preparations very carefully, and if in the slightest doubt telephone the manufacturer.

Verdone, recommended by the Royal Society for the Protection of Birds, has a six-week stipulated safety margin, before allowing it to be grazed. I have also found it less than effective with really strong weeds of waste ground type, such as rose bay willow herb.

Lastly, but by no means least, is the use of the nylon-corded light portable 'weed-eaters' or 'strimmer' type of electrical lawn edge trimmer. This can be used to trim off any weeds popping their heads up in the nursery pens (where spraying is most risky) from docks to brambles, and in place of long-handled shears, to keep the whole establishment as neat as can be. Just as valuable is the fact that the head can be so easily raised or lowered to take off just the top of the grass, if it is getting too coarse, and thereby maintain it in the perfect condition for geese. The instrument itself is so light to hold that it is suitable for anyone to use, and quite perfect for all poultry-keepers.

The Americans use geese as weeders in the mint and cotton plantations. The facts are that, when properly managed, geese

Flock of Sebastopols (Christopher Marler). Note the curled breast feathers and general 'Roman' type of head. Although bred in Romania in grey and buff, white is universally the most popular colour.

are very good weeders, but only if there is nothing more succulent to eat. They must be brought up from goslinghood to eat young weeds, and never allowed to discover the delights of grass or vegetables. In dry, hot areas grass is often hard to find and so the system will work well, as the geese will have no choice but to eat weeds or starve, at least during the day. They are far less likely to eat weeds in cool, wettish regions where grass grows well.

Even so, unless they are indeed going to die of starvation, after their day's weeding is over, they will need supplementary well-balanced pellets or mash in the evenings to grow at all, because of the low nutritional value of weeds.

It is essential to place water containers in a fresh place at the beginning of each day, if they are to weed amongst rows of crops, otherwise the geese will habitually gather in one place and destroy or spoil the crop in that vicinity. The Americans, who use weeding geese most successfully, do so until 4 weeks before Christmas, when they are then sent to the fattening pens and yards for ad-lib feeding, to prepare them for the table.

For most of us European goose-owners, it is still very much a matter of doing the weeding ourselves. Once the weeds have been brought under control, we can turn our attention to improving the quality of the grass itself. Goose manure has an acidic long-term effect on the soil, so that liming, by hand if need be, is an effective treatment every 3 years or so, at 4 cwt per acre. I do not recommend liming more frequently as, although it encourages nutritious clover to grow in the sward, it also discourages the finer grasses, and the effect can be to promote lush but coarse varieties not entirely suited to goslings or adults.

Limestone penetrates very slowly into the soil, and does not suffer much from leaching, so that one treatment lasts a long time. On normal soils about 4 cwt of lime an acre will keep grass and clover in the best balance for goose grazing.

An application of an all-in-one complete granulated fertilizer such as Growmore, applied in the spring of each year, gives the soil and grass an oft-needed boost. The ideal for normal soils is 2–3 cwt per acre and is best applied just before steady rain is forecast; then the geese may be allowed to remain on the grass. If there are more than 2 inches of grass on the area, the granules will fall through to soil level and the geese will not touch them; if a bare area of sparse grass, keep them off until the granules have substantially dissolved.

There are two ways of finding out whether your soil is normal or not. Firstly, one can buy a DIY kit of soil-testers from gardening shops, which is cheap and easy to use. If the results read a pH of about 6.0, then no liming is needed; if less than pH 6.0, then it is. The second way of having your soil analysed is to send samples to your local branch of the Ministry of Agriculture, Fisheries and Food (MAFF). They provide an excellent and truly comprehensive service for those who have problem pastures, and moreover give for a further fee information on whether trace elements such as boron, manganese or cobalt are lacking in your soils and therefore in your grass feed.

Deficiencies of the above minerals tend to occur more frequently on hill country, as sheepmen well know, but soils on certain bedrocks may suffer from the lack of an essential mineral too. MAFF also advise on how to treat the grassland, as part of their services. Happily most people do have normal soils, and often all that is needed is for the bare patches to be re-seeded to make the whole into a perfect greensward. On a pH 6.0 soil, any proprietary lawnseed mixture, containing a proportion of ryegrass, will be perfect for geese.

If you are aiming at as cheap but good feeding for your birds as possible, it is worth looking to a good local seeds merchant for some of the higher protein types of grasses suited to your locality. The S.23 variety of ryegrass is very nutritious, as is the newly-introduced Bensun type of Blue Grass. This latter has a protein content of up to 28 per cent at its very best, under ideal circumstances; under average conditions about 20 per cent. It needs to be mixed with another variety to give the best results for grazing, as it is a fine grass and not very tough-wearing. Keep the geese penned off from the re-seeded areas until well established. Remember that once a fairly decent greensward has been achieved, the geese themselves will help enormously in improving the pasture by manuring it.

Buying weed-treated turves is another quick way of covering large bare areas. Although some would consider it an expensive way, by the time you have considered wild birds eating the seeds, and the time it takes for re-seeded areas to get growing well, I think it compares quite well for cost. If weed-treated, leave for 3 weeks before putting the geese on the newly-turved area.

It is still an oft-repeated fallacy that geese foul grazing so much that other animals will not graze with them or after them. This would only occur, as with any type of livestock, if too many are squashed on far too small an area, making the ground a solid mass of droppings. Indeed, rather than spoil pasture, geese vastly improve it. They harbour the fewest parasites, worms, etc. than any other domesticated animal. Goose droppings, although voluminous in output, do not attract the house-fly or members of the blue-bottle family, and are washed away speedily in a shower, enriching the soil. There is no health hazard of any kind in keeping them.

As for running geese on grass, with or after other animals, the introduction of a house cow, or a sheep or two, is actually to be recommended. The cow will only eat the taller ends of the grass; the sheep will graze lower down; the geese will be very pleased to have the short grass left; while any ducks will busy themselves eating many of the larvae and parasites, which sheep especially suffer from, thus clearing the pasture of pests. Such are the advantages of what has been called 'old-fashioned mixed farming'. Try to keep goose pasture below 4 inches in height. This is because the percentages of protein, calcium and phosphorus are highest in the young growth of grass. All birds prefer short herbage, and once grass has reached the seeding stage geese will barely touch it. Secondly, the largest breeds may become crop-bound, with long, tough grass impacted and stuck in the gizzard. Although a cure is possible if this does happen, it involves a great deal of trouble and the bird gets very thin, because it stops eating once the blockage occurs. The remaining and important objective in keeping the grass below 4 inches is that it curtails the life cycle of the gizzard worm, and reduces the possibility of the geese becoming a prey to it.

Possibly you will want to keep your geese in the orchard. The windfalls (which they like) and plenty of shade make this a good place for them. Be careful with very young fruit trees or low branches. Geese love chewing at young saplings or old wood that they can get their beaks to stretch round. Make a 3-foot high wire netting roll ($1\frac{1}{2}$-inch gauge is as large as can efficiently protect the wood) and place round the young tree trunks.

With old apple-laden branches, prop up wherever you can, as chewing the bark can cause canker to set in afterwards. Once the trunk diameters reach 3 inches or more, the problem is past. As for old wood, we always leave an old rotting log lying temptingly around the edge of the orchard. The geese direct most of their attentions to that; they may even derive some trace elements from chewing it.

There are very few plants in the UK which are really toxic for geese, and usually they are left well alone by adult stock; they are, however, worth mentioning. Firstly, there is the foxglove (*Digitalis purpurea*). Foxgloves prefer acidic, cool, damp locations. Adults never seem to eat them. Always take the precaution, however, of seeing that the young goslings are not penned where they can reach them. All the hemlock family are left well alone, including Fool's Parsley (*Aethusa cynapium*) and Lords and Ladies (*Arum maculatum*). Ragwort is another matter. Ragwort (*Senecio jacobaea*) is very poisonous to cattle, and though sheep are unaffected when grazing the plant at a young stage, geese are not so immune. The danger lies in it being accidentally ingested if it occurs with any frequency among the grass, so pull it up whenever you see it.

Geese seem very intelligent about eating berries. They love gooseberries (of course!) and raspberries and blackcurrants etc., but ignore ivy, yew, pyracantha and holly berries. Actually it is the yew leaves, not the berries, which are poisonous, but I have never known geese to eat leaves either. They will chew bark from the yew, so the trunks need a wire netting protection.

I can find no information, and have no experience of geese eating Deadly Nightshade (*Atropa belladonna*). This plant flourishes on wet, calcareous soils, and it would pay to check round the place for it, before letting your geese into the area. They very rarely eat toadstools or mushrooms. Another advantage is that, if the lawn is good, they very seldom touch the flower beds.

[11]
Fattening, Killing, Plucking, Feathers

FATTENING

There are two traditional times when geese are fattened; in the autumn (Michaelmas) and for Christmas. Michaelmas geese (or green geese) are usually 3–6 months old. If they have been started off well from hatch, on plentiful nutritious foods, and then put on to excellent grass, they can reach a reasonable weight for their respective breeds at a low cost. Nevertheless, their weights will be considerably less than those of adult, fattened geese at Christmas time. There is very little likelihood of these autumn geese becoming plump at this early age, as they are still growing up and building muscle, but they do make very tender eating.

There is no reason why large Toulouse and Embdens cannot be killed at an even earlier age. We have eaten 7–8 week-old Toulouse, and they were a most tender meal, sufficient for a really good Sunday lunch for four people, but they had been reared on the very best unlimited foods beforehand. With such very young geese, there is the difficulty that their pin-feathers are not easy to pluck out cleanly, but on the other hand the best age to slaughter in order to have least trouble when plucking has always been an arbitrary matter.

The best age to kill geese for the table is 6–10 months old, not older if it can be avoided. Too many geese sold for Christmas are over a year old, in fact some are even breeders of 2 or 3 years old, and the corresponding toughness of such birds puts off the customer from ever having goose again. It does every goose-keeper a disservice in the long run. Such older birds, just like older hens, need special treatment in order to be enjoyable to eat. They should be confined to a small run on grass for 4 weeks, and quite apart from their fattening rations should be given drinking water with cider vinegar mixed into it as the only water available. The proportions should be 2 tablespoons of cider vinegar to 1 gallon of water. This has a tenderizing effect upon the meat; boiling is then advisable, rather than roasting.

At 6–10 months all geese except Chinas respond to fattening up, the large breeds and large strains responding best of all, and will make tender and delicious roasts. Confine the birds to a much smaller area than previously, on grass if possible. On good grass, a pen 20 ft by 20 ft per 10 geese would be about right. If the ground is slightly sloping to give better drainage, so much the better.

Try to keep the whole area undisturbed by dogs, children or the movements of farm machinery, and, for security, within ear-shot of the house. Do not lock the geese into boxes or darkened sheds. Not only will they suffer in spirits, but by pining under such unnatural conditions they will stop eating and negate the whole principle.

Running water sufficient to have a wash and a drink helps keep their plumage and health in the best condition. Crowding geese together for 4 weeks brings an increasing risk of goose cholera, as the pen may become very fouled. Try using one of the nursery pens, in disuse at this time of year, and if the grass is getting too awful move them into the next nursery pen on fresh grass. At night, drive them very slowly and quietly into their usual housing.

If running water is not available, 3 gallon-sized buckets full will suffice for 10 geese to last for 12 hours or so. Scrub these carefully before setting down again the next morning, as with the food troughs also.

Set down plentiful coarse sand or fine gravel to aid in digestion; they will eat more if they have access to it. If you are fattening more than 10 geese, ask your veterinary surgeon to help with an anti-biotic or sulphonamide to add to the drinking water. If all the grass has gone by fattening time, for large numbers of geese concrete or gravel yards (sloping for drainage and cleaning) are best. Try

American Buff goose (Mr Collinson).
This young goose shows a good depth
of paunch and a smooth round breast.

to prevent the formation of small puddles in the pen, as these fill
with goose droppings and will become a health hazard, if they
drink from them.

Feed ad-lib all, or some, of the following foodstuffs. Barley meal,
rolled barley, white or yellow maize, unmedicated growers' mash
with a quarter content of either maize or barley; broiler finisher
mash, potatoes, and any milks, liquid, skimmed or dried to make
the whole into a damp crumbly mash. Do not use wheat, as it is
both expensive and forms too glutenous a mass in the gut to be
very satisfactory; it gives a 'full-up' feeling to the geese and they
stop continuously eating, which is not desirable.

There are various combinations which seem to be consumed
with vigour. Barley meal is a favourite, and this, with the addition
of rolled barley to give a bit of texture, produces a plump, white-
fleshed meaty bird.

Yellow maize (corn) tends to give a yellow tinge to the flesh,
but it can be utilized to very good effect until the very last week
of fattening. Maize can be fed whole, but will have to be boiled as
it is too large and hard to be swallowed easily. If you have an Aga
it is economical to boil whole maize. If you have not, it is not

advisable as it takes a slow 2–3 hours before becoming really soft. It is really better to buy broken (kibbled) maize, maize flakes or maize meal for economy and quickness.

Mix any of these with barley meal, rolled barley, broiler finishers or unmedicated growers. Potatoes (see Chapter 5) should not form more than 30 per cent of the total mix, as the high potassium content makes the goose droppings very liquid and quickly makes their quarters very dirty indeed.

Much depends on the breed and the owner's preferences as to what you feed. If the geese have been reared on growers pellets until recently, it may be best to start their fattening diet with growers, plus a good addition of barley meal and potatoes (cooked), moistened with milk. Then, if accepted, gradually reduce the growers, increase the barley content and perhaps add kibbled maize as well. Boiled root vegetables, such as carrots, swedes and turnips, stale bread and cakes can all be most usefully incorporated. Select what is convenient and suits your pocket; all these suggested foods have a high carbohydrate content suitable for fattening.

Give the new feed mixture a week before altering it radically, so as not to put off the geese. Fatten for no more than 4 weeks before slaughter, as this is the optimum period of intake for food for confined geese, and there will be a steady falling-off in consumption from that time onwards.

KILLING

Withdraw all food on the day they are going to be killed, but leave water before them. There are three main methods of killing; whichever way you choose will be unpleasant, but do not lose courage half-way through, as it would only prolong the end for the bird.

The first method is to use a broom handle, placed on the ground, with a foot firmly on one end of it. Have a helper cross the bird's wings over at the back to stop flapping, then lay its neck under the handle, top of head uppermost, just where the head joins the neck. Have the head pointing away from your body. Place your other foot on the opposite end of the handle so that the whole handle pinions down the neck to the ground, then pull the body strongly up and towards yourself. The neck should break, forming a space between head and neck into which blood can drain. I must warn that it sometimes takes some considerable strength to do this quickly, and should always be done by the strongest person present.

The second method is to tie the bird's legs together and hang it upside down from a beam in the garage or barn. With a stout stick, knock the bird unconscious with a heavy blow; then with a sharp, pointed knife open the beak and thrust the knife upwards in the mouth, at a point to the rear of the eyes; then twist the knife sharply sideways, severing the jugular vein. Let the bird bleed into a bucket for 2 or 3 minutes before plucking.

A variation on this is to insert the knife between the windpipe and the muscles of the neck, withe the blade pointing inwards towards the muscles. Push the knife through until the point emerges on the other side; then withdraw. This severs the cartoid artery for a quicker death. A third method is to construct or buy a large metal funnel, which can be nailed to a low beam or bench. Place the goose head-downwards in this: it will not be able to flap its wings in the funnel. Either use a knife as before ('sticking') or simply chop off the head on a block sited conveniently underneath the funnel.

In this method a fairly large amount of blood flows out, and a bucket or similar receptacle should be underneath the block. For the squeamish or for novices, unless under expert guidance, I think to chop off the head with a sharp axe is the best method, because less can go wrong. Once the main blood flow has gone, put a small plastic bag around the neck stump, and fix it round tightly with two rubber bands. In this way, the pluckers will not get into too much of a mess or be too revolted. (See Appendix II).

PLUCKING

Plucking should begin almost immediately. If you have a lot of geese to kill, you must gather your helpers and equipment for the plucking well in advance as, if the plucking is left, and the bird grows cold, it is extremely difficult to remove the feathers.

It is very much easier to pluck geese if they have been dipped into scalding water (60–68 °C—140–155 °F) for 1–3 minutes. The babies' nappies type of boiler, electrically run, is ideal for the job, and old ones can often be bought locally, very cheaply, as people reject them for new automatic washing machines.

Dip the bird in, moving it around in the water by holding its head and feet, and keeping it breast downwards, as the breast has the thickest plumage. If the skin is blotchy when the carcass is plucked, the immersion time has been too long. If the feathers will not come out easily, and the skin is torn, immerse the next bird rather longer. Test on the feathers of the neck where it joins the body; if these stubborn feathers come out easily, the rest certainly will.

Dry plucking is a much more onerous and lengthy way, but it can still be done, if there are two people working on just one goose. Once the bird is scalded, lift out, and either roll it in hot sacks to help dry off a little, or hang it up straight away by one leg at a comfortable level for the pluckers to sit on a bale, and begin at once.

Speed is essential, otherwise the bird cools and the feathers 'set' in again. Place a plastic sheet, or torn-open paper bags, underneath to keep the feathers fairly clean. The object is to leave the skin plucked clean and not torn. Pull out wing and tail feathers and put on one side, first. Then start on the breast; do not rub off fluff, it will tear the skin, especially with Chinas. Try to finish the breast so well that hardly any pin feathers or fluff are left, before moving on to the rest of the bird. Do the wings next, then the legs and then the back.

When the bird is finished, hang it up near a stove to dry off. The larger businesses use poultry wax at 71 °C (160 °F), as the method for getting rid of the fluff, but it is also a very good idea for those who intend to slaughter 10 geese or so every year. It leaves a perfect, clean professional-looking carcass, and the wax is re-usable for years to come. The hot wax can be strained through metal or cloth sieves to remove the fluff, or it can be allowed to get quite cold and set, when the rubbish sinks to the bottom of the slab, and can be cut off easily.

[93]

If you are waxing, have cold water on hand, and once the bird has been dipped in the wax transfer it to the cold-water container to form a skin. Repeat this twice, until a thick enough skin has been formed for easy peeling off. Start peeling when the wax on the body feels vaguely sticky, not when it has gone cold and brittle. Keep these used bits and pieces of wax on one side, if there are many geese to process, as to put them back into the wax vat would lower the temperature rapidly for a while and delay the speed of the operation. The pieces can be remelted at the end of the wax treatment to form a single slab once more.

If the whole prospect of waxing is a bit too much on top of the scalding, there are other time-worn ways of doing it. Do not use candles or paper to burn off fluff, as it blackens the skin. Methylated spirits in a saucer is a good method. Rotate the bird over the flame gently. Propane gas torches or alcohol burning torches are good, too. Once the bird has been de-fluffed it is ready to be dressed.

Large geese usually lose about 25 per cent of their live weight after dressing, medium breeds about 30 per cent, and small breeds about 35 per cent. Take out the innards, when the bird is still warm; the liver, heart and gizzards are cleaned and usually wrapped in plastic or paper with the neck bone, to be put back inside the body cavity, for the buyer to make gravy out of later.

Leave the finished, dressed birds to cool down; if these birds are going to be sold, wrap neatly in transparent wrapping such as 'cling wrap' and affix a label with dressed weight, and your brand name on it. Home-made labels are often very appealing, and they help to establish your good product in the eye and mind of the general public.

If you are going to be freezing the geese for other meals to come, not just Christmas dinner, then proceed according to the instructions given in your freezer books for chickens and turkeys. Goose flesh is excellent for freezing, as it does not dry out, as turkey flesh so often does, and can replace far more expensive Sunday lunches of beef, pork and lamb, throughout the coming year. Weight for weight, it has the highest protein and vitamin content of any meat, including those named above.

Added to the satisfaction of having a freezer full of tender geese, there is a bonus in the form of feathers. Once, keeping geese was almost as important for the feathers it produced as for the meat for the table. Pillows, mattresses, cushions, and many so-called 'eiderdowns' were filled with soft curly goose feathers; more especially so as the true eider down, from the eider duck, was and is most difficult and expensive to obtain. Then came the advent of unlimited central heating, and man-made fibres, which reduced the down-feather demand enormously. Today the demand has shot up again as we look to our looming energy crisis. Sleeping bags, climbing clothes, quilted waistcoats and jackets, survival equipment, pillows and duvets are once again being filled with goose feathers, which are one of the lightest and warmest insulating materials in the world.

For those who are killing their own geese, these feathers are free; or they find a ready market amongst friends, neighbours, Women's Institute groups and garment-makers. The hard feathers from wings and tail, which have already been put aside, can make dusters (on a stick) for home use and are marvellous for manipulating and sorting through bees in their bee hives. Toys and sports manufacturers are often interested in buying a reasonable quantity of these stiff feathers for Red Indian head-dresses, and arrows, or even shuttlecocks.

To prepare the soft downy feathers, put into a sink of cool water, with a dessertspoonful of salt if they are covered with much blood, and a small quantity of liquid detergent, not enough to raise any kind of bubbles. Agitate well and rinse in further cold water. Squeeze by hand and put into an old but sound pillowcase until nearly full. Tie the top tightly with string, and place in the spin-drier. Never put feathers loose in any machine, as they will certainly clog it up.

Once spun-dry. the feathers can be left in their own old pillow-cases and hung up in an airy barn or garage until at least half dry, when they can then be brought into the kitchen or box-room, or large airing cupboard, for final airing. It is essential to turn and fluff up the feathers in the pillowcases twice a day, to ensure that all the feathers have a chance to dry off.

An alternative method is to place the feathers on panels or screens, raised above floor level in an outbuilding, and to turn them daily. The drawback to this method is that in hot weather flies may be attracted to the feathers. A muslin cover should be paid over the screens to prevent this happening.

Using the nursery brooding lamps aids the drying process, or if it is to be done on a large scale fan heaters are excellent. Chinas give at best $\frac{1}{4}$ lb of down by Christmas, Embdens and Toulouse about $\frac{1}{2}$ lb, and to give a useful guide a normal-sized pillow would need $1\frac{1}{2}$ lb of goose down, a single duvet about 4 lb, a quilted waistcoat about $\frac{1}{2}$ lb. Once the feathers are completely dry, they are best stored in plastic bags, paper sacks, or cardboard boxes, sealed up, where they can be kept indefinitely in a dry place.

Live plucking, originating with the Romans, is done extensively in Canada, and of course is still carried on in Europe, although not in the UK. This is done several times before the Christmas slaughter; at 9–12 weeks, and from then on every 9 weeks until they are killed. Without feathers, the geese eat much more to keep up their body heat, and so they finish at higher body weights for killing. There is no doubt that this is a painful experience for the geese, and I do not condone such a practice.

Embden geese.

White Chinese geese.

Domestic Chinese goose; threat display whilst sitting on eggs.

Pomeranian Greyback geese.

Brecon Buff geese.

Toulouse geese.

An exhibition Toulouse.

Fawn Chinese geese.

Roman geese.

Sebastopol geese.

Embden goose and goslings.

[12]
Breeds: Large Division

There are ten internationally known breeds of domestic geese, which will be described in the following chapters, and a number of very important national or local ones which will be dealt with in Chapter 15. These internationally-known breeds divide into categories according to size.

1) The large breed division includes all breeds, both male and female, which should weigh 20 lb and over at maturity. These are: African; Embden (Emden, Bremen, Hanover); Toulouse.

2) The medium-weight division (see Chapter 13) includes all breeds, both male and female, which should weigh 15 lb and over at maturity. These are: American Buff; Brecon Buff; Pilgrim (West of England); Pomeranian.

3) The light-weight division (see Chapter 14) includes all breeds, both male and female, which should weigh 9 lb and over at maturity. These are: Sebastopol (Sevastopol, Danubian); Roman; Chinas (both varieties).

All these domestic breeds have originated in fairly isolated settings, and in areas completely suited to wild geese. These areas are mostly between latitudes 40°N and 60°N, on wide, lowland river valleys, in the broad-leaved deciduous forests and meadows of Europe and Russia. Chinas are a little different in that their home range includes not only the valleys of the Hwang Ho and the Yellow River but also considerable parts of the lower areas of the Gobi desert.

In Western Europe, goose-keeping is not so universal as it was before the Industrial Revolution; much common grazing land was enclosed in that period. During the last decade, however, there has been an upsurge of interest, especially in the keeping of pure breeds.

AFRICAN

This beautiful goose is nearly as big as both Embdens and Toulouse; indeed it is sometimes heavier. It has been called the Barbary, Muscovy and Guinea goose, but appears to be a variant of the Brown China, as both revert to a common type and colour. Certainly, the colouring of both is nearly identical. In recent years a white African has been bred, and most interestingly this

Quartet of exhibition Africans (Christopher Marler). This shows clearly the massive heads and over-all heavyweight appearance. Small refined birds should not be included in a breeding flock.

variety looks extremely similar to the Kholmogorsk white geese of Russia, so perhaps the earlier name of Muscovy was apt. Whether there is a connection with Kholmogorsk or not is debatable, but only the Chinas, Africans and Kholmogorsk do have knobs on the juncture of the upper beak and the head and this would point to *Anser cygnoides* (Chinese Swan Goose) as a common ancestor.

The dewlap has not come from cross-breeding with Toulouse, as very early nineteenth-century illustrations show Africans with their characteristic slight thin crescent-shaped dewlap long before the Toulouse had developed any dewlap, as a breed, at all. In recent years, in the USA in particular, Africans have been crossed with Toulouse to give increased size, but it has also tended to give the African a keel and low paunch, which is undesirable for breed standards. They should have no keel and a firm paunch.

They have a most attractive dark brown stripe running from the top of the head down the neck to join the top of the shoulders. These neck feathers are imbricated—that is scale-like in the way they lie—and not swirling diagonally round the neck as in Embdens and Toulouse.

The young do not have dewlaps. They develop these very slowly until they reach full size at 3 years old. If the dewlap develops too quickly and becomes too large, the bird often develops too large a paunch, and a keel as well. They have dark pin feathers, and so do not dress off so nicely as white and pale feathered geese.

Pick large birds with heavy heads, necks and legs or else they may revert back to little more than China size. They are moderate layers, 20–30 eggs, and are good mothers, but both male and female need shelter if the temperature falls to freezing point, as knobs and feet can be permanently damaged by frost. They have an unusual calling voice.

Description. Weighs 20 lb as an adult, 16 lb at a year old.

Head. Large, with broad crown. Bill (or beak) stout, medium length, deep at the base, with a large, forward-leaning knob on the upper beak where it joins the head. Eyes, watchful, large, rather overhung by the crown.

Neck. Fairly long, thick and showing an arch, although not so extreme as Chinas. Dewlap crescent-shaped, not wrinkled.

[99]

Trio of White Africans (Christopher Marler). Note the smooth underlines of the bodies, and the well-developed dewlaps in these mature large white birds. Knobs are not as large as in Brown (or Grey) Africans, and in young birds the dewlaps will be small.

Back. Straight, flat, with little tapering towards the tail.

Tail. Medium length, tightly closed and kept at a high angle.

Wings. Powerful, folded quite high up and crossing in front of the tail.

Body. Almost rectangular in outline, a smooth underline free from keel, and parallel to the back. The breast carried well up, wide and prominent, the paunch not very large and not baggy and loose.

Legs. Medium length and sturdy.

Plumage. Close fitting and tight over the whole body except for the paunch.

Carriage. Body carried rather defiantly at an angle of about $35°$, active and agile.

[100]

Colour. Head and neck are light ashy brown with a broad dark russet brown stripe running from the knob, over the crown of the head and down the full length of the back of the neck. Beak and knob are black. Eyes are dark brown. The back, tail, wing bows, coverts, sides and upper part of the lower thighs are ashy brown edged with a paler shade. Secondaries are dark grey, edged with a lighter shade. Primaries are dark slate, and the primary coverts are a lighter slate grey. The breast is a light ashy brown, graduating to a lighter tone under the body. The body is almost whitish in tone. The lower part of the thighs are pale and the paunch is white. Legs and feet are a darkish orange.

The white variety is pure white all over, with beak and knobs orange, legs and feet orange, and with light blue eyes.

Avoid. Small birds, too delicate features, too heavy droopy paunches, convoluted dewlaps, no dewlaps in adults, no knob, or knobs standing straight upwards. White feathers in primaries or secondaries (other than in White Africans), broken colour in dark areas or pale neck stripe.

EMBDEN (EMDEN, BREMEN, HANOVER)

Embdens of good strain are truly magnificent birds. They are frequently as large or larger than Toulouse, and weights of 34 lb have been recorded more than once. They have snow-white plumage and have descended from the common white goose of the eighteenth century; they are hardy, vigorous and provide an early maturing gosling for Michaelmas. They dress nicely, as they have no dark pin feathers, and should attain a 20 lb deadweight at Christmas time.

The ganders are very good for crossing purposes as they are very active, and are frequently crossed with Toulouse, Roman, and even Chinas. The female lays about 10 eggs in her first season, but then increases her production to 20–40 according to strain, when mature. She will continue to lay about 25 eggs up to her 15th year, but this total progressively falls beyond that point.

After the first season, there is excellent fertility, and goslings hatch well. The goose makes a good mother, and sits fairly

Embden gander (Christopher Marler). This young bird shows the proud stance and sturdy set of the strong legs required for the breed.

reliably. The goslings are not auto-sexing as such, but a number of females do have a darker greenish-grey fluff across their backs than males do. One gander can be put successfully with three females, but they can fly rather well, so if you wish to contain them and stop them mixing with other breeds, they will need more substantial and higher fencing. They tend to be fairly noisy, or at the least their call is very strident, and therefore they have their drawbacks for small suburban gardens.

They have been extensively crossed, over the last 50 years, and unfortunately many white geese of very mediocre size and shape are today called Embdens, quite wrongly. The comparison between the real breed and these white geese is startling, as the latter are usually barely half the size of the former. See the parent stock before buying this breed and look for size.

The breed originated in the north-west part of the north German lowlands, along the valleys of the rivers Ems and Aller, and in east Friesland (home of the Friesian cow and the East Friesland milking sheep). It is an area of moor and heath, interspersed with wide river valleys, and centres on the town of Hanover today.

Large flock of Embdens (Vernon Jackson). Notice the very large powerful build of these geese, with their broad smooth undercarriages, straight, strong necks and alert bearing.

They are first mentioned by Bonington Moubray in *Ornamental Domestic Poultry* as being imported, possibly for the first time, into England in 1815. It may well be, however, that isolated small importations would have taken place before 1815, as Hanover had the same monarchs as England (the Georges and William) from 1714 to 1837, and there would have been a small amount of intertravel between the two countries during that time.

Nevertheless, the further mention of larger-scale Embden imports in 1815 ('of very uncommon size' as they were described at that time) were a direct result of the end of the Napoleonic war and Waterloo. By that date the Prussians, our allies, ruled over the whole Hanover area including East Friesland, and extending almost to Waterloo itself in the west, as part of their reward for helping in the fight against Napoleon.

The British, who co-operated closely with the Prussians, saw, bartered and ate some of these impressive geese from the region, as part of their 'feed off the land' victualling; they are mentioned on existing documents. It seems very probable that the sudden influx to England of these geese, in the year hostilities ended, was a direct result of their being admired and coveted by several well-to-do officers of the British Army serving there.

These imported Embdens were shipped through the port of Emden at the mouth of the river Ems, and through Bremerhaven at the mouth of the Aller, and one shipment at least came into England by way of Harwich; a fitting destination, as poultry-rearing and breeding has always been important in East Anglia.

By 1820, Embdens (the name had been anglicized) were imported into the USA for the first time. This first importer was a James Sisson of Rhode Island, and he shortly exhibited his birds in the many keenly-supported poultry shows of the area.

It is interesting that, although contrary to today's breed requirements, both the early English imported Embdens and those of the Americans frequently had pinkish rather than orange beaks and legs, showing that they had certainly had an admixture of eastern Greylag as well as possibly Pink-footed, White-fronted and Lesser White-fronted genes at some past distant time, as all winter in the identical area. This pink colour was not as definite as that of the Pomeranian goose further to the east, and has been almost completely bred out of Embdens in all countries now.

Once in the hands of English and American breeders, the size of the imported breed was greatly increased; by 1872 weights of well over 30 lb were common, and by 1929 the breed standard was set at 30–34 lb for ganders, 26 lb for geese. Sadly, it is now difficult to find many Embdens which weigh so much. Toulouse may have been used to increase the original bodyweight, or English Whites, Greys and Saddlebacks, as very occasionally Embdens have a single dark grey or nearly black feather in the wing, up to their first moult. If it persists after this, the bird concerned ought to be carefully monitored so that the owner can see if this is passed on to any offspring. If the offspring do inherit this fault, plus a few more dark feathers, the parent bird should be sold for crossing purposes. Because of their white plumage, swimming water is necessary to keep them looking spruce. They are excellent foragers and will wander rather far if not constrained.

Quartet of Embdens (Mrs A. A. Starey). The wide breast and back desirable in a good Embden are clearly shown.

Watch out for your vegetable garden as they will eat almost everything in it.

Description. Today's best ganders will attain a weight of 30 lb at maturity, geese 26 lb.

Head. Rather oblong, large but not too massive, beak joins smoothly to head, medium length, not too convex a culmen. Eyes alert and sometimes aggressive-looking.

Neck. Long, not too slender, carried upright with only a slight curve, no dewlap as such but larger and older birds are permitted a fullness under the throat.

Back. Straight from shoulder to tail.

Tail. Quite long, closely folded, kept on a level with the back.

Wings. Very large and strong, with primaries crossing in front of the tail on the back.

Body. Long, slightly triangular viewed side on, with the paunch at the widest end of the triangle. Broad across the shoulders, plump, wide and rounded breast smoothly blending into the paunch. The paunch should be clear of the ground and square.

Legs. Sturdy, medium length, very strong looking.

Plumage. Firm, smooth, close feathering except on paunch, but even there not loose as in Toulouse.

Carriage. Ganders elevated at front to about 45°, females much less so, but still far from horizontal. Very proud.

Colour. Beak, feet, legs bright orange, with an off-white bean at the end of the beak. Eyes light clear blue.

Avoid. Keels on breasts, single-lobed unbalanced paunches, small body size, too short legs, grey or black feathers in mature geese.

TOULOUSE

These are the mammoths of the goose world, and yet are perhaps the best suited for a small garden and for the family pets. They have a large keel, a gullet and a large paunch, and the general over-all sideways shape is massively rectangular. Because of their great size they are not as active as other breeds, and hardly need fencing in to stop them wandering. Indeed, of all geese, they are probably the most domesticated and home-loving; they know quite well that they are too big to escape from dangers quickly,

Toulouse gander (Christopher Marler). The full keel, and the loose feathering required on the back and paunch, are clearly seen here, with a nice upward tilt to the tail.

as they rarely fly, and this draws them close to the homestead. They are very quiet and rarely aggressive.

For the person interested in breeding geese, they offer an interesting challenge, as they are not so easy to breed from as other geese, and at the same time there are many breed requirements for the perfect bird that are difficult to get. Building up a breeding flock can bring enormous pleasure and interest throughout the whole year, as Toulouse develop fairly slowly, and are still growing up to 2 years old in some of the best strains.

With other smaller breeds, by 4 months or so the owner knows they will not grow much more, and the breeder's season is, in a sense, over. With Toulouse every week that passes bring a growth and change to look for, so that one's interest never flags. This is particularly the case with regard to breeding for large size, and for deep keels. Keels develop, according to strain, from 6 weeks to 5 months old, but if there is no sign of a keel at 9 months there is not going to be one, and the bird is useless to breed from, and should be eaten. If too many goslings in each batch fail to develop keels, it very probably points to some previous misguided cross-breeding with Embdens, and the parents are not quite pure. Pure-bred Toulouse will produce at least 8 out of every 10 goslings with a keel of varying size, and with careful selection for the breeding stock may well produce keels on every bird.

Both the keel and the dewlap are signs of feed convertibility, and it usually follows that the birds with these features well developed will be large in size also. The keel is not a flap of loose skin; it should be wider as it goes back towards the paunch, with which it should join smoothly, and when killed off and dressed the keel falls back onto the breast as extra meat. Because of the dark plumage, Toulouse have dark pin feathers and darker flesh, which makes them more suitable for family eating; they are delicious, with a more definite flavour, and can be killed at 7 weeks, if they have been well fed previously. At this age, they would very adequately feed a family of four, and they would weigh about 7 lb, ready for the table.

Ganders are slower to mature than other goose-breeds and may show little interest in mating until a year old, but it is quite untrue that even when mature Toulouse ganders are too big or lethargic to mate properly. Ganders of 26 lb can mate with little difficulty, even without swimming water to help them. What will put off Toulouse when mating is when they are run with a large flock composed of other more active and interfering breeds; they do like peace and quiet. One gander to one or two females is advised, and pair matings are the most successful of all, as Toulouse ganders become very devoted and faithful to just one goose as the years pass by, so that a second female may become progressively ignored, with the owner believing it is because the gander is not fertile or capable.

Some Toulouse geese are good mothers, but many are not. If you would like to encourage your goose to stick to the task, help her by offering dry bedding, in a cosy corner of her house. Talk to her when you go to visit her during the day, and generally soothe her, as Toulouse are easily deflected from broodiness. Do

Flock of exhibition Toulouse (John Hall). Notice the deep paunches, even-sided, touching the ground between the legs, and also the long, filled-out bodies of this mature flock.

not allow any other females to bother her, and you may well have success.

Females lay 40–60 eggs, except in their first season, when 15–20 is the norm. They lay increasingly more eggs from 2 to 8 years old, and then very gradually will lay 1 or 2 less every successive year. Even so, Toulouse of 100 years of age have been documented as still laying 10–15 eggs a year! They lay 40 per cent better than Embdens, and this was the basic reason why they have been crossed with Embdens, and so frequently. By putting an Embden gander with a prolific Toulouse goose, one could expect far more goslings. Pure Toulouse eggs have about a 50 per cent hatchability; Embden × Toulouse have about an 80 per cent, so this cross has much to offer those in the table-meat market. (Pure Embden eggs have about a 60 per cent hatchability for the largest strains.)

They need the very best feeding from hatch to about 5 months of age; after that their food consumption falls off rapidly, and from that age onwards they will grow slowly on just good grass alone. Once adult, they eat far less than almost any other goose, but they will be severely stunted if not allowed ad-lib top-protein-level foods to begin with. They do not forage so efficiently as Embdens, and should not be allowed to eat the coarse long grasses at all, as these may impact in the gullet and cause a stoppage. They thrive best on lawn grasses and seem to escape gizzard worm by so doing, where the Embden seems more prone, eating the ranker herbage.

When buying adults, give the birds time to relax and get used to your presence before selecting, as fear makes the gander, in particular, draw himself up, and this in turn pulls the keel out of shape. Bear in mind that although they often look bigger than Embdens this is partly because of their loose feathering, and they may not weigh as much. If all other breed requirements are satisfied, choose a long-bodied bird over a short-bodied one; there is more potential for size in future offspring.

They originated in the Haute Garonne in France, over the wide valley of the river Garonne and its tributaries; they were and are the most popular goose in the *départements* of Haute Garonne, Tarn et Garonne, and Gers, and the most famous in all of France.

Eight-month-old Toulouse (bred by the author). The slight hollows, at the point where the keel joins the paunch, fill out as the young Toulouse reach a year old.

The area centres on the ancient town of Toulouse, and the famous grey goose of Toulouse is mentioned (in connection with *pâté de foie gras*) as early as the fifteenth century. Toulouse *foie gras* was sent to Paris and also up the Rhône-Saône valley to Strasbourg at that time; Strasbourg is one of the two major *foie gras* producers today in France, but the Toulouse goose is no longer used for the industry. That dubious honour now goes to the smaller grey Alsace goose, in that area.

Nevertheless, when the first Toulouse geese were sent to England and the USA, the old export route that had been used for hundreds of years previously was used. From the town of Toulouse, the geese were shipped along the Canal du Midi, through the Carcassone gap in the mountains to Marseilles. This was why the goose was originally called the Mediterranean or Marseilles goose.

The 13th Lord Derby imported Toulouse into England for the

first time in 1840. He was the President of the Zoological Society at that time, and had formed an extensive menagerie at Knowsley, for which he sent out agents to collect from all over the world. The magnificent and comprehensive domestic poultry, including the Toulouse and other geese, were dispersed to private collectors (at his death in 1851), who continued to concentrate on developing the breed.

They were by no means the large birds they are today; their weights were around 18 lb at that time, but such was the general interest in poultry and waterfowl breeding in Victorian times that they had reached consistent weights of 30 lb by the 1870s, and in 1894 a 34-lb bird won its section at the National Poultry Show in London. There have been reports of some Toulouse reaching 40 lb. It is possible that they were crossed with English Greys, who had reached a similar 18-lb standard weight at that time, and who certainly consistently developed full paunches, but now we shall never know for sure. I doubt whether Embdens were deliberately used to upgrade the size, as such a crossing so often breeds out the big bowed-out keel. Toulouse were first shown in the USA, at Albany County, New York Fair in 1856, so we can assume that the breed entered the country at least 2 or 3 years previously. They have since become a most popular and sought-after breed. From Boxford, Massachusetts, we have a substantiated record of a Toulouse goose in one family for 101 years, passed down from father to daughter, who was sitting on 15 eggs at that advanced age when she was kicked by a horse and killed. The famous 'Madam Goose', again a Toulouse, owned by Robert Schomp of New Jersey, laid 6 eggs (of which 3 hatched successfully) in her 85th year.

Today, they are very popular in European countries, especially Germany, as well as their country of origin. In the USA, buff Toulouse have been bred, very true to type. The beginner must be very careful not to buy just any grey goose. There is only the colouring in common between grey geese and Toulouse.

Description. Weights: Adult ganders 28 to 30 lb; adult geese 20 to 22 lb.

Head. Very massive, deep, wide across crown of head, in older birds the sides of the face become a little fluted. Beak medium length, sturdy, with a slight rise of the culmen to make a 'Roman' outline. Eyes interested, set in a little.

Neck. Thick, medium-to-short, very slight curvature. Dewlap medium to large, convoluted, extending quite far down the throat.

Back. As broad as possible, not as broad as Embdens, long, horizontal to slightly convex lengthwise.

Tail. Average length, quite well spread, carried at a high angle to form one smooth continuous line from the paunch upwards and outwards.

Wings. Medium-tight folded, very large, folded with tips crossing well over the back in front of the tail.

Body. Very deep and massive, with very good length. Keel very bowed in front, and very full and deep as it goes underneath the body. A smooth juncture of keel with paunch, without large hollows at that point, on either side of the keel. The underside of the keel should ideally be horizontal with the ground. The paunch should touch the ground and have wide evenly developed joined lobes.

Legs. Hardly to be seen in the best specimens, but of medium length, hidden by the thigh coverts.

Plumage. Soft and loose, with the exception of the flights. Very profuse.

Carriage. Very dignified and horizontal; both back and under-.carriage parallel with the ground.

Colour.

Head. Dark blue-grey. Beak clear pale orange, with off white bean in adults, dark bean in young especially females. Eyes hazel or dark brown.

Neck. Dark grey, lighter at front, dewlap light grey.

Back. Dark grey, edged with lighter grey to white, rump blue-grey.

Tail. Mainly white, with wide dark grey band across the feathers.

Wings. All feathers, except primaries, are dark grey, edged with light grey or white. Primaries very dark grey to black.

Body. Upper parts dark grey edged with white, except flanks, where the white edging predominates. Breast light grey, shading paler still until the undercarriage including paunch and stern is completely white. *Thighs.* Beneath thigh coverts, light grey; large thigh coverts dark grey, boldly edged with white—paler in young birds up to first moult. *Legs.* Orange to reddish-orange. *Avoid.* Small snipey heads, refined necks, narrow crowns, no dewlaps on birds over 1 year of age, twisted keels, unbalanced paunches, white around base of beak in young (a little is allowed in adults) no keels (over 9 months old) shallow paunches, wrong colourings, too upright a stance when in repose, tight feathering.

[13]
Breeds: Medium-Weight Division

AMERICAN BUFF

This is one of the two breeds of geese of American origin. Part of the foundation stock is believed to have come from Pomerania in 1900 and this appears very probable. Pomerania is in that area of eastern Germany where their well-known domestic Pomeranian geese have such pronouncedly reddish-pink or reddish-orange beaks and legs. This area shelters even today four wild species in the winter time, all of which either have pink legs (eastern Greylag, Pink-footed) or pinkish-red beaks (eastern Greylag, Lesser White-fronted and White-fronted) or both.

Although American breed standard requirements are now for orange beaks and legs, for many years after the breed was founded in the USA pinkish-red was the norm, and only by careful breeding and selection has this been altered. Even so, recessive genes still throw up a bird with the wrong colouring today.

Pomeranians more often produce buffs or buff-backs than any of the other main breeds; this may well be linked to the beige-brown feathering of the above-mentioned wild geese, who have plainly played their part in forming the domestic breed. American Buffs are of similar size to the Pomeranians, about 18 lb for the ganders, and this has always been a popular size in both Europe and the USA. They are very hardy, fairly good natured, plump and substantial. Their pin feathers are pale and leave an attractive dressed carcass, and their outer plumage is very practical, as it does not show dirt so noticeably as all-white feathering. Apart from pinkish-red recessive-gene-carrying birds, they do

American Buffs (Mr Collinson). The gander in the foreground clearly shows the long body and rangy appearance of this breed, which distinguishes it from the slightly more refined Brecon Buffs.

occasionally produce a buff-back; this is like an English Saddleback or a buff Pomeranian.

If female offspring show a greying of their feathers, the use of a paler buff gander to mate with them removes this factor. The buff plumage tends to fade in the sun, and also before the moult, and if you intend to show them they must be kept continually in the shade to prevent this happening, and allowed plenty of green food.

They should be larger and coarser than their English counterparts, the Brecon Buffs, and they then ideally satisfy the medium to large bird demand.

Description.

Head. Oval and moderately large. Beak strong, evenly tapered, stout at base. Eyes alert, moderately large, fairly prominent.

Neck. Moderate length, slightly curved, held upright, with no dewlap, but a fullness under the beak is allowed.

Back. Medium length, very slightly convex, width carried well back, flat and broad across the shoulders.

Wings. Wide-feathered, moderate size, smoothly folded, crossed over neatly at the back.

[116]

Body. Free of keel, but broad and plump and full. Paunch moderately deep and slightly baggy, with uniformly developed dual lobes.

Legs. Medium length of sturdy build.

Plumage. Hard, smooth and tight-fitting except for the looser feathering of the paunch.

Carriage. Stance held at about 25° above horizontal, less for females, slightly aggressive in attitude.

Colour. The pattern markings are identical to those of Toulouse, except that the coloured areas are a fawny beige shade of buff, instead of grey, and with a lighter lacing to the feathers just as in Toulouse.

> *Beak.* Bright orange with flesh coloured bean, no dark blemishes.
>
> *Eyes.* Brown.
>
> *Legs and feet.* Orange to orange-yellow.

Avoid. Reddish or deep pink coloured beaks, legs, feet. Very varied mottled-coloured feathers in the buff parts, grey tinge to the buff areas, white flights in Buffs proper (but allowed in buff-backs). Blue eyes.

BRECON BUFF

The first Brecon Buffs were bred by Sir Rhys Llewellyn in 1928 from some buff geese found on a Breconshire hill farm. The breed was recognized by the Poultry Club in 1934. Like the American Buff, the colourings are similar to Toulouse, except that the grey areas are buff, but unlike the American Buff the English (or Welsh) variety is built on more delicate, lighter lines, and should show a general refinement of features. The gander should weigh about 16 lb, the goose about 15 lb.

As it is the 'odd goose out' in England, with its pinkish-red or deep pink legs and beak, it seems difficult to account for, as it is unlikely that Welsh hill farmers would have imported Pomeranian blood into their strain, until it is noted that wild species of geese which have deep pink-coloured beaks and legs are frequent wintering visitors to Wales, and even occasionally stop the year

Brecon gander (G. Allen). Notice the smooth breast but fairly full paunch of this attractive Brecon Buff gander.

Brecon Buffs (G. Allen). The plump appearance of this flock well illustrates the useful table-qualities of this medium-sized breed.

round. Buff-tinged feathering is also a common feature of these wintering wild geese, and there may have been some cross-breeding between them and an English goose at an earlier period.

It is a medium-sized, light-boned, good laying bird, rather quiet in disposition, and very attractive to look at. It dresses off very well, as all geese with pink-coloured extremities do, and is a good forager.

Description.
Head. Fine, never coarse. Beak smoothly tapering. Eyes bold.
Neck. Fairly long, held in upright, slightly curved stance, no dewlap.
Back. Quite broad, good length, straight from shoulder to tail.
Tail. Average length, tightly folded, carried level with back.
Body. Quite broad, well-rounded. Breast round, plump, no keel. Paunch quite wide, square, carried well off the ground.
Wings. Moderately large, tips crossing over in front of the tail.
Legs. Medium length, moderately fine bone structure.
Plumage. Firm, smooth, moderately loose on paunch but not profuse.
Colour. Beak, legs, feet deep or reddish, eyes brown.
Plumage. Exactly like the American Buff, including light edges to feathers.
Avoid. Large heads, heavy necks, orange feet, legs and beak, white primaries, grey or mottled plumage.

PILGRIM (AND WEST OF ENGLAND)

These two breeds of geese are the only truly auto-sexing ones at hatch, and are therefore rather special. I shall start with the English West of England geese first, as not only were they a long-established breed many centuries before the American Pilgrims made their official appearance but there has recently been some confusion over the names and the origins of both of them.

Long before European colonists went out to America, certainly before A.D. 1600, the English had evolved a breed of geese which were auto-sexing. The gander was always yellow at hatch, growing up into a predominantly white bird, and the geese were always

West of England goose and gander (Peter Hayford). A typical goose (on the left) and gander. The females have various-sized patches of grey on their plumage, but are mainly white. The ganders are always white.

greyish at hatch, growing into either predominantly grey or grey and white birds.

In 1620, the Pilgrim Fathers went over to live in America on several ships, the *Mayflower* being the most famous; they were mainly West-Country people, and they sailed from Plymouth. They took with them every tool, article and commodity they could, including a number of English geese as well as other stock, and these are mentioned on bills of lading for the voyage. These geese were not called Pilgrims before sailing, or by the settlers when they reached America; it was the name given by later emigrating English to those geese they saw on New England farmsteads, and this is commonly regarded as being the first reference to 'Pilgrim' geese.

In both countries these auto-sexing birds prospered and even in 1800 in England the Reverend Jenyn wrote in his *Vertebrate Animals* that these geese were still auto-sexing, and there were no other breeds well in existence in the country at that date. By 1815, however, the introduction of Embdens in largish numbers affected the auto-sexing because of cross-breeding between the two, and Toulouse later on added to the crossings, so that by 1900 the original English geese had mostly lost their auto-sexing, especially in the eastern areas of England where most of the new foreign geese had become popular. Exactly the same process occurred in the USA, with the loss of a sex-linked genotype in their geese.

In the West of England, however, always more cut off from new influences, these useful geese were still common and numerous on farms and small-holdings up to 1960 or so. Since then, sadly, there has been a marked decline in numbers and they (genuine 100 per cent auto-sexing) are hard to find now.

Meanwhile in America, Oscar Grow, the famous waterfowl breeder, originated from his stock a 'new' auto-sexing breed which he called 'Pilgrim' after the transferral of his Iowan home to Missouri in 1930. These are the true Pilgrims, and the English variety is correctly called West of England; but the word Pilgrim is often tacked on to West of England, perhaps because they are rather similar in appearance.

The (American) Pilgrim is rather smaller than the English

Pilgrim goose. It will be noticed how much more all-over grey this female is, compared to the West of England goose. White patches develop around the eyes as they reach a year old, and the tone of grey on the body lightens.

Pilgrim gander. Pilgrims can be distinguished from Embdens, as they are built on a smaller scale. At the same time, they cannot easily be confused with Romans, as they are not so short-legged and chubby.

goose, and has rather paler grey colouring in the females, and West of England females often show more of a saddleback effect of grey marking than the American birds do. They both are prolific layers, sturdy, excellent foragers, and make a popular size of table-bird. To confuse matters further, several batches of Pilgrims have been imported into England in the 1970s from the USA.

It is most interesting that in Normandy, France, they have what appears to be identical West of England geese, which they claim to have kept for hundreds of years. It is true that in 1066 William, Duke of Normandy, became William the Conqueror of England, and the two countries were united for the next 200 years. During that time, William's best fighters and supporters were awarded knighthoods and English estates if they would uproot and stay with him in England. Many of them chose to remove from Normandy to England, lock, stock and barrel—perhaps geese too. They certainly brought over their larger livestock. Or did the Normans see English geese and take them back to friends and relatives? We cannot know, but the close geographical locations of both the Normandy and the English geese make some connection likely.

Description. Weights 16 lb adult Pilgrim gander, 13 lb goose (slightly heavier for West of England)

Head. Oblong, sturdy. Beak quite stout, eyes alert.

Neck. Medium long, strong, quite thick, curved slightly.

Back. Rather flat.

Tail. Short, on same plane as back.

Wings. Large, strong, tightly folded.

Body. Deep, round, plump, breast prominent, without keel in young, but often with in older females. Paunch quite deep, dual-lobed, clear of ground.

Legs. Plump thighs, strong medium length legs.

Plumage. Firm, smooth.

Carriage. Only slightly elevated.

Colour. Beak orange, whitish bean, eyes grey-blue (or brown for females), feet and legs orange-yellow.

Plumage. Pure white (for ganders) except for barely noticeable light grey over the rump, or sometimes wings and tail, but not much grey allowed.

Head. (Females) mainly grey in young, with small areas of white, which increase as bird ages. Beak orange, legs, feet orangey yellow, eyes brown.

Neck. (Females) medium grey with some white allowed.

Plumage remaining. Pilgrim females: markings as in Toulouse, but the all-over tone of grey is much lighter, more dove grey.

West of England females: grey saddleback markings.

Avoid. Pink beaks, legs; single, unbalanced or twisted paunches, solid dark feathering in ganders, white flights or complete absence of white on heads of adult females, small size.

[123]

POMERANIAN

This goose originates in Pomorze, a region to the extreme east of Germany between the rivers Vistula and Oder. It is a mostly flat, low lying, marshy area, some of which has been brought under cultivation. There are many lakes and streams surrounded by moors which attract wild geese in thousands even today. Five species of wild geese frequent the region, and the variety of the Greylag is the eastern, hence the pinkish-red beak and legs of the Pomeranian. It has been left alone as an area, because the Oder and the Vistula and their tributaries have always formed natural barriers to strangers, and this has tended to isolate the Pomeranian farming community, and allowed their breed of geese to establish itself well. Today it is a very popular breed, not just in Pomorze but in much of northern Germany and Poland, and has been imported into the USA. The geese are grey (similar to Toulouse in markings), white, and the most popular, Saddleback. They have deep pinkish-red beaks, legs and feet and, unusually, a single-lobed paunch. It is quite a heavy bird: ganders weigh 17–18 lb and geese 15 lb. There is very little crown to the head.

Pomeranian goose (M. Jarominski). This standard saddleback-marked Pomeranian is the most popular variety of the breed in Poland today. The markings are consistently reproduced in both male and female, with the head and neck always mainly grey. Note the single-lobed paunch.

[124]

It is a good layer (about 60–80 eggs), has good pale meat, is hardy even under extremely cold conditions, and fertility is good.

It is basically a most useful commercial breed, which is reminiscent of English Saddlebacks, but leg, beak and foot colourings, plus the single-lobed paunch, point to a quite separate evolution very early on in history in their own comparatively isolated areas (in the case of the UK an island).

Description.

Head. Flattened crown, fairly broad, but refined when viewed side on. Beak, strong slightly concave culmen. Eyes large and quite prominent.

Neck. Strong, upright, average length, no dewlap.

Back. Slightly convex lengthwards, moderate length.

Tail. Short, horizontally carried.

Wings. Smoothly and tightly folded, carried high up.

Body. No keel, plump and wide breast, with no bow. Paunch wide, fairly deep but tapering to a single lobe at the base.

Legs. Quite finely boned, medium length.

Plumage. Not profuse, quite tight all over.

Carriage. Almost horizontal, calm and placid looking.

Colour (Saddleback variety).

Head and neck. All head and upper neck dark grey, lower neck white. Beak deep pinkish-red, eyes blue.

Back. Rump bluish-grey, front section grey edged with white.

Tail. Mainly white, with broad band of grey across the base.

Wings. Flight, tertials and lower edges are white; from above causes grey area to look roughly heart-shaped. The rest of plumage is white, except for thigh coverts which are grey edged with white. All the coloured areas are very bold and clearly defined. White and grey Pomeranians look like Embdens and Toulouse respectively (in colour), except for the pinkish-red beak and feet of the Pomeranian.

Avoid. Orange or yellow extremities, dewlaps, dual-lobed paunches, very pale coloured areas.

[14]
Breeds: Light-Weight Division

CHINA

This is the most ornamental domestic goose of all, and is very graceful to look at. The breed originated (as did Brown Chinas) from the China Swan Goose (*Anser cygnoides*) which breeds in Siberia, and Upper Mongolia, and winters in the river valleys of northern China.

These geese were first generally seen during the Opium Wars between Britain and China, in 1839–42, when China, previously cut off from and hostile to the rest of the world, was forced to open five of her main ports to foreign traffic. As a result, in 1848, Alfred Whittaker of Beckington, Somerset, was the first China importer for his private flock; some geese hatched on board the sailing ship, which brought both Brown and White Chinas from the port of Shanghai. Another flock went to the Royal Park of St James.

The Americans also imported Chinas at much the same time, Fletcher Webster of Massachusetts being the first importer on record. Many subsequent importations of this goose came through Hong Kong, which the Chinese had had to cede to the British at the end of the wars, hence the name 'Hong Kong goose', as it has sometimes been called.

By the 1880s the interest in them died down in England as the Victorians were then aiming for great size in poultry, and Chinas were not suitable for their plans. Reginald Appleyard, the famous waterfowl breeder, was one of the first breeders in this present century to re-kindle an interest in Chinas, especially White

Brown (Grey) Chinas (Christopher Marler). Note the beautiful markings and elegant carriage. Ganders have the larger knobs on their beaks.

Chinas, which he obtained as 'sports' from his Browns (the first White Chinas to be shown in this century at the World's Poultry Congress in London in 1930). Appleyard's birds were heavier than today's preferences; they laid 40–100 eggs and were up to 13 lb in weight. They are now very popular in the UK and the USA, but less so in France, Germany and eastern Europe.

They have had their genetic part to play in forming Russian geese. Chinese travellers of the eighteenth century mention seeing them there in a semi-wild state, returning south for the winter. They are illustrated as being knobless and therefore still wild; but they are Brown Chinas. Sanchez, travelling among Cossack villages in 1736, says the peasant girls used to call to the geese as they came south, and their own geese would return to them. They love water, but keep clean well without it, with their tight plumage; their feathers do not curl on the neck as in many

White China gander (John Hall). This shows the smooth, short plumage and gracefully curving neck required for the breed.

European varieties. They are excellent layers, up to 100 eggs being quite usual, good sitters and mothers, and often lay a second batch in the autumn. One gander to five females is satisfactory, and the eggs hatch well in incubators. They will begin laying at 5 months with liberal feeding. They can be sexed at 6 weeks or so, because the knobs of the ganders then show. The knobs which have appeared since domestication suffer from frostbite and will discolour, so they need a little shelter at that time. The knobs do have another disadvantage; they are contrary to Kosher laws, and so Chinas cannot be eaten by people of Jewish faith.

They are very good for crossing purposes, either with Embdens or Romans, but some reluctance is sometimes shown to successful mating with large strain Embdens. Any resultant goslings are fast-growing and medium in size. They will eat young weeds and are the principal breed used as weeding geese in the USA.

The meat is darker than usual but with a very fine flavour, and not at all fatty; Chinas, however, are not easily plucked. They are delicious but not visually the best. In Brown Chinas the darker pin feathers compound the problems of producing a good dressed appearance. They are good for year-round family eating

[128]

Flock of White Chinas (Mrs Anita-Dawn Allen). The sideways view of the flock shows the shortness of the body length in comparison with non-China breeds.

(remembering there is more waste on a small bird than a large one) but are difficult to sell to the retail or hotel trade. They are just too small to be killed at 8 weeks and do not respond at all well to fattening methods. Chinas are noisy geese.

Description. Adult gander 12 lb, goose 10 lb.

Head. Very refined, neat and slender. Beak evenly tapered with a large round knob at its upper base. Eyes quite large, prominent and alert.

Neck. Long, slender, elegantly held, very gracefully arched.

Back. Short, flat, sloping to tail.

Tail. Very tapered, short, tilting upwards.

Wings. Muscular, carried high, primaries reaching tip of tail.

Body. Short, plump and round, no keels or paunches, breast prominent, carried high, full. Paunch rounded but not drooping or baggy.

Legs. Hocks protrude below thigh coverts, very slightly leggy in appearance, sturdy for their size.

Plumage. Very smooth, tight, neck feathers imbricated.

[129]

Carriage. Semi-erect, aggressive, especially in ganders.
Colour. (Both sexes) beak and knob bright orange, flesh-coloured bean. Eyes blue, legs and feet rich orange. White plumage throughout. Brown variety: beak and knob very dark slate or black, with black bean with a light grey line at the bottom of both features. Eyes brown, feet and legs deep darkish orange. Plumage identical to the African except that where there are any coloured areas they are several shades darker.
Avoid. Oddly shaped knobs, small knobs, short, thick necks, low tails, coarse heads, long backs, horizontal carriage, no knobs, dark feathers in White Chinas, or white feathers in Brown Chinas. Wrong colouring of extremities for each variety.

ROMAN

These are small, chubby white geese, very attractive and very practical as a small table-bird. Although named 'Roman', it is very unlikely that they originated in Rome, as it is not a natural geographical location for the evolution of a goose breed and there is no written or pictorial evidence of geese being kept by Romans before approximately 600 B.C.

It is very probable that this small white breed came from Hungary and Romania, along the wide plains of the Danube river valley, where civilization prior to 1000 B.C. was very advanced, both in farming and metallurgy.

Just after 1000 B.C. Hungarians or Romanians crossed the mountain barrier between their countries and what is now Italy, by way of Ljubljana, and came down through what is now Trieste today. Once there, they conquered the neolithic peoples living in the wide plains of the River Po in Italy, and settled there in their stilt houses along the river for some years. It is known that they brought geese with them; they had kept geese (as they still do) extensively all over the Danubian lands, as pits containing goose bones and other remains have shown.

By about 800 B.C. some of these invaders set off again, south-wards across the Apennine Mountains towards what was to be Rome by 753 B.C. They took their skills in farming and metallurgy with them; it would be surprising if they did not take their geese

Roman gander and goose (G. Allen). The non-aggressive temperament of Roman geese in general can be seen here from the attitudes of the pair.

and animals too. Certainly, within 100 years of this founding of Rome, geese were well established there as both sacred and domestic objects.

Today, in the large goose-rearing Danubian countries, the same goose is frequently found, but in both grey and white. It is fascinating to learn that they may well have taken grey and white Romans with them when they invaded Italy in 1000 B.C., as there are still flocks of grey Romans on those very plains where they built their stilt houses so long ago. They are called Padovan geese, in Padova Province centred today on the city of Padua. These grey and white Romans and the geese from the Danubian lands (including Sebastopol) all have pink or pinkish-orange beaks and legs. They all seem more prone to mutation of their feather structure than many breeds, as tufts or crests or curling feathers appear with some frequency.

Although pure white, they do not resemble the Embden very

[131]

much, as they are not only smaller but have short, fine-boned legs, more delicate heads and beaks and shorter necks. They are docile, mature early, and make a good small goose for Michaelmas. They do well on rough pasture and are excellent grazers. One gander to five females is a suitable ratio, as the ganders are very active. The geese lay 50–100 eggs a year, and the goslings are easy to hatch and rear. They are suitable for crossing with Embdens of medium size; the goslings will grow quickly and be of medium size. The females are moderately good sitters, but on the other hand the eggs hatch out well in incubators.

As table-birds, they dress off nicely with pale flesh and a fairly meaty breast. In some birds grey feathers show on the back; here it is best to do as the Romans did, and breed these out of the flock. They were not imported to England until the beginning of this century, and not imported to the USA until after World War 1. They are now quite popular in both countries.

Flock of Romans (Christopher Marler). These attractive small geese are found in large numbers throughout the Danube Valley and the Balkans.

Description. Adult ganders weigh 12 lb, adult geese 10 lb.
Head. Refined, oval-shaped, shallow crown. Beak medium long, straight and tapering. Eyes watchful but friendly.
Neck. Upright, short, thick and quite straight.
Back. Moderately wide across shoulders, but not long.
Tail. Rather short and blunt, carried level with the back.
Body. Quite deep, over-all plump appearance, rounded breast, round, full paunch, but not too baggy.
Legs. Thighs plump, set wide apart, short legs, finely boned.
Plumage. Fairly close fitting and hard.
Carriage. Almost horizontal to the ground, ganders slightly raised at breast.
Colour. Beak pink to pinkish-orange, white bean. Eyes blue, legs and feet reddish-orange. Plumage white everywhere.
Avoid. Too big a bird, coarseness, too long legs, wrong colourings, yellow beaks.

SEBASTOPOL (OR DANUBIAN)

These unusual and very pretty geese are common in the Black Sea area, and more especially in Romania, Bulgaria, Hungary and Yugoslavia. In Hungary and Romania, the principal countries lying astride the river Danube and its tributaries, there are many flocks kept of white straight-feathered geese of the same size and conformation as the curly-feathered Sebastopols found in the same region. There is little doubt that the curly-feathered Sebastopols are flocks of related birds with feather mutations. They may have been fostered because curling feathers are the very warmest and best for human use. Certainly they are well established as a breed, and breed true to type.

The only variations amongst both types of geese from the Danube are that beak and leg colours become slightly more orangey-red towards the west of the region, and more pinkish-red towards the Black Sea in the east. The European breed standards (unlike the American) demand pinkish-red rather than orange extremities.

[133]

Sebastopol gander (John Hall). The beautiful soft long curling feathering on this gander is what is to be aimed for in this breed.

Both these south-east European countries are major goose-producers today, and may have been amongst the first peoples to domesticate them. It is interesting that in 1300 B.C., 300 years before these Danubians invaded Italy (see the section on Romans), they had invaded Greece via the Morava-Vardar gap in the Balkan mountains. They came as conquering settlers here too; shortly afterwards geese enter into Greek legends (Penelope and her 20 geese in Ithaki) and figure very soon on pottery and artefacts. All these early references to geese are in connection with nobles and kings, not ordinary peasants at all. It therefore seems very probable that they did not evolve in Greece, but were brought by the invaders. There are no references to Sebastopols, so it may be that this curly variety of the Danubian goose is a comparatively recent breed.

Sebastopol goose (Christopher Marler). Note the neat, small head and over-all curly feathering in this young bird.

Sebastopols are medium small white geese with long curling feathers all over, including flight feathers. The breast feathers must be curly but care must be taken that excessively curled feathers there do not cause straight, stiff flight feathers, as there is a tendency for this to happen. They are average layers (30–35), the goslings are very hardy and robust, and they produce an attractive plump table-bird. They are unable to fly and need swimming water to keep clean. They are docile and friendly, useful for meat production and yet ornamental to look at.

They were first imported into England in 1856 after the end of the Crimean War, and subsequent work with them recently, at Hadlow College in Kent, showed that if in-bred using the best curly-feathered birds the plumage that resulted resembled that of silkie fowls. In their countries of origin they are sometimes grey or saddleback, but the preference everywhere is for pure white.

[135]

Description. Adult ganders weigh 12 lb, an adult goose 10 lb.
Head. Round, neat, refined, shallow-crown. Beak medium long,
tapering. Eyes placid and watchful.
Neck. Short, thick, held upright, fairly straight with curly feathers
beginning at the base.
Back. Fairly wide across the shoulders, rather short, and looks
shorter than it is because of the curling plumage.
Wings. All feathers should be curled or spiralled, including flights
and secondaries.
Body. The bird seems spherical; it actually is plump underneath,
and the plumage makes it look very round indeed. Breast full,
plump, prominent, all feathers curled, paunch not visible because
the feathers spiral and curl down over it.
Legs. Short length, fairly fine bone structure, obscured from view.
Plumage. All feathers spiral or curl, including tail, below base of
neck.
Carriage. Horizontal or near horizontal.
Colour. Beak pinkish-red for European breed standards; bright
orange for USA standards. Eyes blue, legs and feet light orange
for USA standards, deep pinkish for European standards. Plumage—pure white desired (in white varieties), goslings sometimes
have pale grey traces, but not allowed as adults.
Avoid. Straight or short plumage anywhere below the neck, wrong
build and coarse heads.

[15]
Other Breeds

These geese were bred in England well before the Roman Con-
quest, and by 1600 were more or less sex-linked (see section on
the Pilgrim and West of England), but by about 1850 the introduction of Embden and Toulouse blood had produced a large
attractive goose, but with a not very reliable sex-linkage, especially over much of the eastern half of the country. Although some
come as white ganders with grey or saddleback females, some are
all white (both sexes) and some have saddleback ganders and
geese. They are about 17 lb for an adult gander, 14 lb for the
goose. The White and Saddleback, as well as the Grey, all tend
to have paunches and some keel in old age and are a plump, very
useful breed. Beaks and legs are orange.

FRENCH TOULOUSE AGRICOLE

A medium-sized goose notable for its looseness and softness of
body. It has been bred especially in this way for the *foie gras* market, as a medium size, loose-bodied goose gives the best enlarge-
ment of the liver when fed intensively. A poor layer (6 eggs or
so in the first season rising to 30 in maturity). Beaks pale pink,
legs pinkish-orange, eyes brown. Looks like a keel-less Toulouse
but on a smaller scale; its use as a *foie gras* goose has diminished
in favour of the Landes recently in the south-west of France.
Ganders weigh 14 lb; geese 12 lb.

Alsace geese (M. Alex Wiltzer). Very similar to grey Romans (Padovans), these geese provide most of the goose liver for the famous Strasbourg *pâté*.

FRENCH LANDES

Similar to the above, with no gullet, but with a fairly big paunch, making it look elliptical viewed sideways on. Orange beak and legs, plumage otherwise like Toulouse. Ganders in this breed can be distinguished at 5 months as they always develop much longer necks, and are rather noticeably aggressive. The females lay 35–45 eggs annually. They weigh 16 lb for mature ganders, 14 lb for geese, and can be fattened up to 22 lb (for ganders). The livers can weigh up to 1½ lb in weight, and go to the ancient town of Perigueux for *foie gras* manufacture.

FRENCH BOURBONNAIS

Almost indistinguishable from Embdens, from which the breed originated. One of the best table-birds in France. Can be killed at 3 months, but best at 6 months. The Bourbonnais Club was founded in 1919. Legs and beaks are reddish-orange, eyes are blue, the head is rather more refined than German Embdens. The body is the same, except that keels are allowed.

FRENCH POITOU

With the Toulouse, this is the best known breed of goose in France. Famous for the quality of their feathers and for goose-skin powder puffs; both are widely exported. They were introduced to Poitiers, under the Dukes of Aquitaine, by Dutch settlers in the town, who wished to make the warm quilted garments that were made at that time in Holland. This developed into an industry based on Poitiers, which has been developed into a very important one. The geese are live-plucked three times a year. Beaks yellow-orange, legs yellow-orange, eyes blue, plumage all-white. Weights 13 lb for adult ganders, 10 lb for geese.

French Poitou (M. Alex Wiltzer). These geese produce very fine quality feathers for quilting and cushions.

GERMAN CELLER

Buff geese originating north-east of Hanover, almost in Pomerania. Identical to American Buffs, but with pinkish-red beaks and legs. Brown eyes. Weights 17 lb ganders, 15 lb geese.

GERMAN STEINBACHER

Fighting geese, light blue and grey, marked like Toulouse, but smaller and with no keels or paunches. Beaks and legs orange, eyes brown. Weights 12 lb ganders, 10 lb geese. Very pugnacious by breeding only.

RUSSIAN TULA

Large grey geese similar to Toulouse; not kept as widely as the other Russian breeds. Originated on the Volga-Vyatskii central area of Russia, just south-east of Moscow. Mostly kept on private holdings attached to collective farms. No figures were given in the Russian 1974 goose census for these geese, but they are the least popular of the breeds. Weights are 23 lb ganders, 18 lb geese. Grey plumage, keels, paunches, but not often with large gullets. Eyes brown.

RUSSIAN ARSAMAS

These geese were once classed as fighting geese, and went to the St Petersburg 'Goose Pit' amongst other arenas, before goose fighting was declared illegal in the early part of this century. They are very hardy, poor to moderate layers (15–25 eggs) and are very similar to Embdens in every particular, except on a smaller scale. They weigh 18 lb for ganders, 16 lb for geese, have all-white plumage, blue eyes, and pinkish-red beaks and legs. They have been bred for muscular strength, and they still are rather tough for table-bird production. There were just over 3000 of these geese at the 1974 census.

Pair of Russian Arsamas (S. Pimenov). This breed is similar to Embdens on a smaller scale, except that there is sometimes a slight rise where the beak joins the head.

RUSSIAN KHOLMOGORSK

This is a most attractive large white goose, and forms by far the greater part of the total of domestic geese in Russia. Mature ganders weigh about 24 lb and females about 20 lb, thus equalling our three largest breeds in the west.

They originated in the fertile cool temperate region lying 600 miles north of the Caspian Sea, and west of the Urals. This region, originally meadow and deciduous forest, is the land cut through by the river Volga and its many tributaries, and geese have been domesticated here for hundreds of years. Kazan is the chief town in the Kholmogorsk-rearing area.

Ganders have an African-shaped knob on their upper beaks, which grows with age; females have a steep rise where a knob would be, but no actual knob. The goslings have imperceptible knobs, under a year old. Beak and leg colouring is reddish to

Flock of Russian Kholmogorsk geese (S. Pimenov). The best Kholmogorsk are those with knobs, dewlaps, deep paunches and good keels, such as the bird in the immediate foreground. They are big attractive birds.

deep orange, eyes are dark brown to black. The head looks massive because apart from the rise or knob, they also have a gullet or dewlap. In older ganders this is convoluted, but not as deep as Toulouse; in younger birds it is smooth and crescent-shaped.

Carriage is horizontal, and both sexes have a deep, double-lobed paunch, and often a small to medium keel. These large plump geese form the major part of the Russian table-bird market, and have proved ideally suited to the changeover to factory-rearing methods adopted in 1968. Their numbers are rapidly increasing. They are, incidentally, the only one of the three Russian breeds to have knobs on their upper beaks.

[16]
Ailments: Prevention and Cure

Provided geese are kept properly, they are hardly ever ill; they are certainly far more healthy than any other domesticated farm animal. Sometimes, however, they do catch something, and that is when you will want to have some idea what to do. For the dosages of the following recommended drugs, see your own veterinary surgeon.

ASPERGILLOSIS

Caused by an *aspergillus* species of fungus, which attacks birds under 6 months old in particular. Symptoms are an increased rate of breathing, with beak held open after the slightest exertion, a general lethargy and a lack of enthusiasm for food, followed by diarrhoea. In a chronic form it affects the lungs and air sacs, and weaker birds may die. Mouldy hay or straw, or mouldy food, are the main causes, so fresh bedding constantly given, and washed food containers, are the best preventatives. If your flock is afflicted, use a farm disinfectant to soak containers in. Griseofulvin may help prevent the disease, or potassium iodide can be used in their rations.

Another respiratory affliction can be caused by putting birds into newly creosoted houses. This also causes heaving chests and gaping beaks, which will continue for 24 hours at least, after their removal from the fumes. Fumes give them sore throats also, and as this puts them off eating it resembles aspergillosis.

CHOLERA (OR PASTEURELLOSIS)

The symptoms are yellowish-green watery droppings, difficulty in breathing, running from the nostrils, burying their beaks in the ground to help keep themselves upright, and in the last stages a tendency for the head and neck to roll backwards over the shoulders in a helpless manner. Cold, damp unsanitary conditions, often with overcrowding, are the main causes, with a lack of vitamins (usually in the form of grass) as a secondary cause. Fattening pens suffer most. If caught early enough, it may be controlled with tetracyclines by injection, or oral treatment with sulphur quinoxaline. Iron sulphate can be added to the drinking water, if birds are to be closely penned, as a simple part-preventative.

SALMONELLA (*Salmonella typhimurium*)

This is very rarely found in geese, but if it is diagnosed the Minister of Health must be informed. There is a very high death rate in the very young, with mopey and dejected behaviour beforehand, and diarrhoea. Shortly after these symptoms comes death. It usually affects most of a flock, and this factor, if it occurs, should prompt a visit from your vet just to make sure what they have all died from. He will take blood samples as well as having post-mortems done. If caught in time, Furazolidone or Tribressin may be given orally to each individual bird, or Trivetrin or Borgal injected. Movement to new housing might help to control the disease, but slaughtering all the affected stock will be necessary.

OPHTHALMIA (SORE EYES)

This may start with a very watery eye, which forms crusts and sores around the eyelids, or with high inflammation of the eye itself. This is caused by a diet poor in vitamins, especially A and C, or a lack of deep enough fresh water for the birds to submerge their heads, or it may be brought into your flock by newly-purchased birds from elsewhere. Scratching makes matters worse and spreads the infection.

Geese suffering from this should be separated from the others, and given higher protein pellets (such as layers), and yeast in a separate water bowl, as well as having access to a deep bucket or container of fresh water with a mild chlorine solution in it, to sterilize. A saline solution can be used to wash the eyes twice daily, or antibiotic drops of Neomycin can be given at night straight onto the affected parts.

PNEUMONIA

This respiratory infection is very common with goslings up to 6 months of age, but rarely so in adults. It often follows another infection, such as colds or aspergillosis, and is most likely to attack goslings who are overcrowded and ill-ventilated in their houses, or on filthy bedding which is keeping them cold and damp. Even chills caught while out in a rain shower can lead to pneumonia in unfeathered young ones. The symptoms are very heavy, laboured breathing, with the beak very wide open so that the tongue protrudes up and forward inside (in the last stages). Wheezing and bubbling can be heard from a yard away, but listen for this by putting your head next to the breast of the bird, before this critical stage is reached. The afflicted goose will hardly eat or drink, and will wave about on its legs when standing. It should be put into separate housing, with clean bedding and even a heat lamp, if there is plenty of high-level ventilation. The goose has about 5 days to live, if it is untreated, from the wheezing stage, but we have saved geese, with our local vet's prompt attention, several times when all looked hopeless, with Lincocin injections, continued over a 5–7 day period. Tetracyclines by injection or Aureomycin soluble powder in small amounts of water and squirted down the patient's throat are other good treatments. The only cautionary note here is that it is vital to continue these treatments for 5–7 days, as too short a course does not kill the infection, which flares up and usually does kill off the sufferer the second time.

COCCIDIOSIS (*Eimeria and Tyzzeria species*)

This is very rarely found in goslings. It causes extreme weakness in very young goslings, with very severe diarrhoea and death. The whole of the vent area is very wet and soiled before death, and the baby bird becomes very emaciated. Treatment is medicating the drinking water with Sulka N or Furizolidone, and dousing the living quarters with a solution of 10 per cent ammonia.

GAPES (*Syngamus* TRACHEAL WORM)

Most frequently acquired from running geese with hens and turkeys, this is a minute hairlike worm infesting the trachea (throat). The symptoms are harsh breathing, opening and shutting the beak, shaking the head excessively from side to side, and frequently giving a cross between a cough and a sneeze. The bird does not lose much weight, does not feel hot about the legs, does not wheeze in the chest region, and seems moderately fit otherwise, thus distinguishing gapes from real respiratory infections. Treat with Thibenzole suspension in water containers or feed.

GIZZARD WORM (*Amidostomum anseris*)

This is the one really harmful worm which attacks geese. It is a hairlike worm which burrows into the lining of the gizzard and impairs its function, often producing ulcers in the gizzard, with a substantial loss of blood. Weakness and anaemia are followed by severe emaciation, as the bird is in much pain and cannot eat. The first signs to look for are listlessness (but with no signs of respiratory trouble) and a hunching up of the head and neck with a general raising of the breast, as in pain. Catch the bird and either take its temperature or feel whether it feels hotter under the feather than a healthy member of the flock. If it is gizzard worm, there will not be an appreciable rise in temperature above normal, and this will help tell you if it is sickening for something quite different. If you use a thermometer, take the temperature through the vent; 39.5 °C (103 °F) is normal for geese.

Unfortunately, once the worm has established itself in young goslings and growers, they succumb very quickly and will die, so their keeper must keep an eye on them daily. Older birds are more resistant. Watch out for rapid weight loss, in particular. Treatment is dosing with Thibenzole suspension over a period of days, or Panachur or Nilverm. These medications can be put in the drinking water, or if the affected birds are too weak to drink much use old hypodermic syringes, without the needles, as squirters for individual dosing.

Birds on running water, and fresh short pasture, are not so frequently afflicted. Move all the geese from their current pen, if you get a bad outbreak, to fresh ground. Do not let them return until after the winter, or when 3 months has elapsed.

Staphylococcus aureus

This is quite a common infection, and can be picked up from the soil as well as from wild birds. It causes severe lameness, often in just one leg, as it attacks the joints and the feet, which swell up and feel burning hot. Diarrhoea often occurs as well. In young birds (under 6 months) if left untreated it can kill, but does respond well to treatment even when quite acute. If older birds go untreated, they may survive, but often with joint deformity and permanent arthritis. It often attacks through small cuts in the feet, so if you notice minor feet wounds keep an eye on the bird for Staphylococcus too. Keep the afflicted bird in an isolated warm-bedded house with plenty of pellets and yeast in water, as both these contain the vitamins to help recovery. The better fed a flock is, the less likely they will be to catch this infection. Treatment is either Tetracyclines by injection, which is especially long-acting, or Terramycin in solution given over a period of at least 6 days, twice a day. Initially a small dose of Dexamethasone will relieve joint pain.

A postscript to this section is that for those with heavy-weight geese check that lameness is not caused by broken toes from inter-gander tussles. The joint will be very swollen and the remainder of the toe will be loose and rubbery when the foot is placed on the ground. We have successfully made a goose-foot template

[147]

into which we strapped the foot with masking tape, placing an old sock over all, and tying the sock round the ankle. It works well on dry grass, but comes adrift if the bird goes into water, and is only worth doing if the bird is very lame and very big. It does set the bone straight, rather than curled, but it is not usually worth the trouble.

OVARIAN TROUBLES

Often caused by double-yolked eggs that have become stuck in the oviduct, but still a rare occurrence in geese. Smear Vaseline round the vent opening and then inject (with needleless hypodermic) 3 ml of olive oil or lambing oil.

GRANULOMAS (CORN-LIKE GROWTHS)

Can occur on the soles of the feet and are painful, so causing the bird to be very lame. Acquired from running the birds on very dry, hard ground. Treatment is to cut out by thermocautery, and then apply disinfectant and firm dressing. Watch out for *Staphylococcus* until the wound is healed, and dress freshly every day.

LEG WEAKNESS

Found in small goslings who are not on good food and good grass soon after hatching, and particularly caused by a shortage of niacin. Feed good high protein foods and yeast in water, and plenty of grass cuttings if it is too cold outside; they will fairly soon recover.

STAGGERS

Not often afflicting goslings. This staggering gait of walking is caused by no drinking water, or too much direct sun and not enough water for their needs.

CROP IMPACTION

This may occasionally occur after coarse grasses or even string have been swallowed and become stuck. The gizzard looks like a swollen football, and feels hard under the hand. The goose will stop eating altogether. It may also be the first sign of gizzard worm infestation. Doses of 1 teaspoon Bicarbonate of Soda in a little water 3 times daily, followed by 1 teaspoon of Liquid Paraffin after each dosing, will usually free the contents of the gizzard. Massage the distended gizzard gently. If the trouble does not go away after 2 days, use a gizzard-worming treatment next. If things still do not improve and the bird is still on its feet, the vet can surgically open the gizzard and remove the obstruction. Geese, especially the smaller breeds, can eat some remarkable things, from buttons to pieces of glass!

CONSTIPATION

Only rarely occurs as a result of geese being shut in with no water and a fibrous cereal, such as oats, to eat. Dose with 1 teaspoon of Liquid Paraffin each.

ANAEMIA

Female geese who have been sitting on eggs a long time sometimes develop anaemia, which manifests itself as a general prolonged weakness. Treat with Ferrous Sulphate at 1 teaspoon per gallon of water, and give pelleted protein feed.

SLIPPED OR TWISTED WINGS (ANGEL WINGS)

Slipped wings may develop after the first moult. The flights droop downwards and tend to fold outside the secondaries, but do not stick out from the body very noticeably. Taping (with masking tape) is fairly satisfactory; pulling out after the flights have finished growing is another method. Twisted wings appear with the growth of the first flight feathers, and (leaving genetics aside) often happen to the biggest, fastest-growing birds. In France, it has been discovered that Toulouse are the worst sufferers. With their huge wings and enormous growth rate, the heavy blood-laden quills are too much for the wing muscles to control.

In other lighter breeds, it may be that this is more of a genetic problem, and if it occurs frequently in offspring they should not be used as breeders. For large-breed owners, do not discard too quickly, especially as something can be done to put this right if caught at once.

The wings turn out at right angles to the body, on the whole flight-feather sections, and cannot be folded at all across the back. It looks unsightly, and birds with both wings affected find it difficult to mate successfully as they cannot use them like arms to balance with.

Treatment must begin as soon as there is the slightest suspicion of angel wing. If it does not, although the treated wing 'sets' well for that season, on the next moult the feathers grow out at right angles again. Tie or tape the ends of the quills moderately loosely together, and run the same string or tape under the wing, over the shoulder and back over the wing to join up with the quills again. Use sticky-backed chiropodists' felt to protect the shoulders (where the wings join the body) from the string cutting in.

Take off the bindings weekly to massage and exercise the wing muscles. This is only worth doing for what looks like being a superb bird, apart from the wing trouble. Alternatively, if expense is no object the affected part of the wing can be surgically removed even in adulthood.

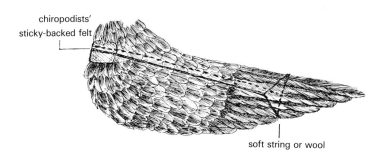

chiropodists'
sticky-backed felt

soft string or wool

How to tie up twisted or 'angel' wings.

DROPPED TONGUE

This is where the floor of the mouth, which lies under the tongue, drops down between the lower jaws. The tongue falls into this pouch, and in severe cases the goose cannot get its tongue up again to eat. Dewlap or gulleted birds such as Africans and Toulouse suffer more than other breeds, but no breed commonly develops dropped tongue.

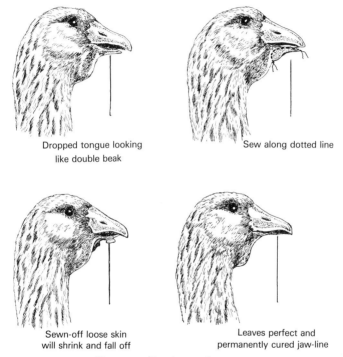

Dropped tongue looking like double beak

Sew along dotted line

Sewn-off loose skin will shrink and fall off

Leaves perfect and permanently cured jaw-line

Treatment for dropped tongue.

It is totally, permanently curable. A quick minor veterinary operation involves the stitching of the loose outer skin hanging down. The skin, which must not include the inner membrane of the floor of the mouth, is strangled by the stitching, as no blood can circulate past it, and the skin withers and falls off. It never comes again. Too fibrous grass, or grains such as oats fed with insufficient water, can help cause dropped tongue in any breed.

[151]

So can putting goslings on such poor quality grass that in order to obtain enough nourishment they must eat frantically; this causes the skin under the jaws to swell up, and food can become lodged there which eventually causes a pocket to form, into which the tongue drops. Only sew off unfeathered under-skin, never too far back towards the throat. Dropped tongue sometimes looks like a double beak viewed sideways.

Appendix I
Metric Conversion Table

Weight

1 oz = 28.4 g
1 lb = 0.454 kg
1 cwt = 50.8 kg

Area

1 acre = 0.405 hectares

Length

1 in = 25.4 mm
1 ft = 304 mm
1 yd = 914 mm

Capacity

1 pint = 0.568 litres
1 gallon = 4.546 litres

Appendix II
Slaughter of Poultry

It is extremely important that no bird awaiting slaughter should be caused unnecessary pain or distress and that the method of killing should be efficient and rapid. It is also important that no regulation or law is broken in respect of killing the birds. Always obtain the fullest and clearest advice on this aspect. [For example, in the UK, the best and most current information is obtainable from the National Farmers' Union (British Poultry Federation) and the Environmental Health Officers Association. Their Code of Practice (revised 1988) for on-farm slaughter and marketing of poultry provides all relevant details: legal requirements, practical implementation (including correct holding pens, killing and cleaning), equipment, personal hygiene, refuse and storage. It is available in booklet form, at modest cost, from any local branch of the NFU; but always crosscheck with the relevant local Environmental Health Department for regional variations of regulations.]

For small holders and farmers selling extensively, it is also advisable to check the available information on salmonella in breeding and hatching from the appropriate source. [In the UK, this would be the Regional Poultry Federation.]

In addition, most member countries of the EC will also be subject to its current and planned regulations relating to slaughter.

Overall, it must be stressed that it is not at all easy to kill a full-grown goose. Expert advice really is *essential* in order to avoid cruelty.

For regulations in Europe and the USA, apply to the appropriate Department of Agriculture.

Index